W B Yeats
Images of a Poet

48   W. B. Yeats broadcasting, 1937
Courtesy of the B.B.C.

W B Yeats
Images of a Poet

My permanent or impermanent images

by D J Gordon
with contributions by Ian Fletcher, Frank Kermode and
Robin Skelton

Manchester University Press

Barnes and Noble Inc New York

© 1961 The University of Manchester

Published on behalf of the University of Manchester
by Manchester University Press
316–324 Oxford Road
Manchester M13 9NR

First published 1961
Reprinted 1970

ISBN 0 7190 0355 5

USA
Barnes & Noble Inc.
105 Fifth Avenue
New York, N.Y. 10003

USA SBN 389–01055–3

Printed in Great Britain by Butler & Tanner Ltd, Frome and London

PREFACE

The purposes of this book will best be understood if its title is taken in a double sense. It deals first with the images Yeats used in his poetry, which, as the works of Mr Henn, Professor Melchiori and others have shown, were frequently of visual origin. No student of Yeats would dispute that there are aspects of his work which cannot be properly understood without information of the kind here made easily accessible.

Each theme is discursively treated in a preliminary essay, but the book is also a catalogue of the Exhibition of the same title shown in Manchester in May 1961, and in Dublin during the following month. This larger enterprise grew out of a purely photographic exhibition held in Reading University in 1957. The duplicated Guide of 1957, compiled by Professor D. J. Gordon with the assistance of Ian Fletcher and myself, has proved useful to scholars, but is no longer obtainable. The present volume is a version of the Guide, greatly expanded and entirely re-written by Professor Gordon, with help from the same hands and from Robin Skelton.

Frank Kermode
John Edward Taylor Professor of English Literature,
University of Manchester

May 1961.

ACKNOWLEDGEMENTS

Professor D. J. Gordon and Mr Ian Fletcher would like to thank the Research Board of the University of Reading, which has made much of their work possible; Mrs M. I. Dilks and Miss Margaret Fuller, so much of whose work went into the preparation of the Reading Exhibition; their pupils, Miss Valerie Barnett, Mr Brian Farnham and Mr John Lucas; and also Mrs J. Chennells, all of whom have given much time to tedious jobs.

Lady Albery; Mrs K. Bridgewater; Professor Hugo Buchthal; Alvin Langdon Coburn; Miss E. Collett; Miss Elizabeth Coxhead; Albert van Dalsum; R. O. Dougan; Mr & Mrs J. Eades; Mrs Franklin; John Gawsworth; Mrs Patricia Greacen; Lady Gore-Booth; George Goyder; Anthony S. Heal; T. R. Henn; the late Joseph Hone and Mrs Hone; Augustus John, O M, R A; Mrs Mary Kennedy; Hildo Krop; the late Henry Lamb, R A; Dr R. Lhombraud; Mrs Mac-Bride; Mrs Mary Macnamara; David Masson; Miss Nettleship; Miss Ursula Nettleship; Mrs D. P. O'Brien; Miss Mary Pollard; the late Lennox Robinson; Richard Southern; Dr J. Todhunter; A. Toher; F. Wilson; Miss Anne Yeats; Gerald Yorke.

Valentine Iremonger, Esq, and the Embassy of the Irish Republic, London; The French Embassy, London; The Royal Netherlands Embassy, London; The Swedish Embassy, London; Ian Scott-Kilvert, Esq, and the British Council, Paris; The Arts Council of Great Britain; Mervyn Wall, and An Chomairle Ealaion, Dublin; The Department of External Affairs, Dublin; Ernest Blythe, and the Abbey Theatre, Dublin; D. McGreevy, and the Building Centre, Dublin; The Irish Tourist Board; The Librarian and Deputy Librarian, Trinity College, Dublin; The Librarian of Archbishop Marsh's College, Dublin; The Librarian and Sub-Librarian, Brotherton Library, University of Leeds; The County Librarian, Sligo; The Borough Librarian, Acton; The Warden and Fellows of Winchester College, and the Librarian of the College; The British Broadcasting Corporation; The Courtauld Institute of Art, University of London; and the Warburg Institute, University of London.

The Directors and staffs of the following Museums and Art Galleries: Amsterdam, Stedelijk Museum; The Belfast Museum and Art Gallery; The British Museum; The Fitzwilliam Museum, Cambridge; The Municipal Gallery of Modern Art, Dublin; The National Gallery of Ireland, Dublin; The Glasgow Art Gallery and Museum; Leeds City Art Gallery; Le Musée du Louvre, Paris; Manchester City Art Gallery; The Metropolitan Museum of Art, New York; The National Gallery; The National Portrait Gallery; Norwich Castle Museum; The Lady Lever Art Gallery, Port Sunlight; The Tate Gallery; The Victoria & Albert Museum.

As far as possible acknowledgements have been made to photographers or sources of prints under each catalogue entry though, in some cases, this information has not been traceable. Where no such acknowledgement is included, the print has been made by the University of Reading's photographer.

LIST OF LENDERS TO THE W. B. YEATS EXHIBITION

Mrs W. B. Yeats: 1, 10, 13, 23, 25, 53, 131, 136, 140-144
Abbey Theatre, Dublin: 44, 70, 127a, 136a, 144a
Amsterdam, Stedelijk Museum: 167-171
Belfast Museum and Art Gallery: 2
Cambridge, Fitzwilliam Museum: 21, 237, 245
Cox, Arthur, Esq: 35
Dublin, Municipal Gallery of Modern Art: 8, 11, 37, 69, 73, 76, 80, 89
Dublin, National Gallery of Ireland: 12, 14, 82, 93, 196a, 197
Glasgow Art Gallery and Museum: 43
Gordon, Professor D. J.: 81, 236
Horniman Museum and Library: 146
Kennedy, Mrs M.: 291, 292
Leeds City Art Gallery: 36
Manchester City Art Gallery: 31
Manchester University, Whitworth Art Gallery: 145, 207, 208, 209, 224
225, 238, 281, 282, 285-288, 290, 296
National Portrait Gallery: 33, 217, 218
Norwich Museums: 229, 230
O'Brien, Mrs D. P.: 68
Port Sunlight, Lady Lever Art Gallery: 278
Reading University: 29, 30, 119, 120, 126, 148-150, 201, 215, 216
220-223, 259-275, 279, 280, 289, 305, 309, 316
Tate Gallery: 28, 32
Victoria & Albert Museum: 276, 283, 284

LIST OF CONTENTS

THE IMAGE OF THE POET

1865-1939

'Style, personality – deliberately adopted and therefore a mask – is the only escape from the hot-faced bargainers and the money-changers.'

W. B. Yeats

In October or early November of 1886 Gerard Manley Hopkins, then in Dublin, called on John Butler Yeats. Hopkins seems, naturally enough, to have been rather embarrassed when the painter gave him, 'with some emphasis of manner' a pamphlet containing a poem by his son. This was *Mosada*, reprinted from *The Dublin Review,* Yeats's first book, and a legendary rarity. It has, Hopkins says, in a letter to Patmore, 'a portrait of the author by J. B. Yeats, himself; the young man having finely-cut intellectual features and his father being a fine draughtsman. For a young man's pamphlet this was something too much; but you will understand a father's feeling.'

The *Mosada* drawing (1) is the first of a series of drawings and portraits by his father that runs until 1908, when the old man went to New York. It is this series that dominates our first section, counter-pointed with photographs and other artists' versions of the young poet's face. Dominates, in the sense that it is a series, by one hand, and that a father's. In fact it is curiously indecisive. It may be that a father who has been drawing his son since he was a baby in arms,[1] is not the best interpreter of his progress to maturity or of his adult image; and Yeats himself said that his father had always seen him through a mist of domestic emotion. Yet there was Titus and his father; and it may be that J. B. Yeats was simply not a good enough painter; or the indecisiveness may be a reflection of the temperament that made it almost impossible for him to complete any portrait at all or to control the result. The *Mosada* drawing and the portrait done three years later in 1889 by H. M. Paget, a minor artist and a neighbour in Bedford Park (2),[2] show a well set-up, handsome enough, bourgeois young man, who might, in Paget's case, have appeared in a not very good Renoir. But they stand apart. In so far

7

as there is a general impression left by J. B. Yeats's later versions, (7, 8, 9, 10, 12, 13, 14, 23) it is of refinement, physical fragility, withdrawal, and, not to avoid the word, weakness. It is significant that, unless the artist had told us, we should find it difficult to date or arrange the portraits chronologically; the face changes so little. They certainly suggest the poet.

Yeats was conscious enough of his role as poet and aware of dressing the part. In 1889 Katherine Tynan described him: 'in looks, Mr Yeats is as picturesque as one could desire – hair, beard and beautiful eyes of a southern darkness, with a face of a fine oval, and a clear, dusky colour. Nature has written the poet upon his face.' What nature had written was a description of a poet of a certain kind, the conventional poet of Bohemia, aestheticism and the Twilight. Writing about the Rhymers' Club in his *Autobiographies,* Yeats remembered that only he, Le Gallienne and Arthur Symons, the three provincials, wore any costume but 'that of an English gentleman.' Le Gallienne had a loose tie and, though Yeats does not mention this, his hair amounted to a parody. (Le Gallienne's dress, in fact, (6) shows its origin quite clearly: it is a workaday version of Oscar Wilde's early aesthetic costume). Symons had an Inverness cape 'quite new and almost fashionable.' He himself wore 'a brown velveteen coat, a loose tie, and a very old Inverness cape, discarded by his father twenty years before.' To George Moore, writing in *Ave* out of imperfect memory and imperfect sympathy, Yeats at this time suggested the provincial aping a tedious French literary fashion:

> 'When I saw him he was on exhibition, striding to and forth at the back of the dress circle, a long black cloak drooping from his shoulders, a soft black sombrero on his head, a voluminous black silk tie flowing from his collar, loose black trousers dragging untidily over his long, heavy feet – a man of such excessive appearance that I could not do otherwise – could I? – than to mistake him for an Irish parody of the poetry that I had seen all my life strutting its rhythmic way in the alleys of the Luxembourg Gardens, preening its rhymes by the fountains, excessive in habit and gait.'

The eager and engaging boy of the Lafayette photograph – the first published photograph of Yeats and in the first book about the Irish Literary Movement, Ryan's *Irish Literary Revival* – (1894) wears the tie and velveteen coat (3). The Inverness cape is added in one of the snapshots taken by his countryman, fellow member of the Rhymers and collaborator in the Literary Movement, T. W. Rolleston, in his

Hampstead garden in that same year, 1894 (5). This is the Yeats whom George Moore described as Alick, poet and mystic, in *Evelyn Innes* (1898).

> 'He had one of those long Irish faces, all in a straight line, with flat, slightly hollow cheeks, and a long chin. It was clean shaven, and a heavy lock of black hair was always falling over his eyes. It was his eyes that gave its sombre ecstatic character to his face. They were large, dark, deeply set, singularly shaped, and they seemed to smoulder like fires in caves, leaping and sinking out of the darkness. He was a tall, thin young man, and he wore a black jacket and a large, blue necktie, tied with the ends hanging loose over his coat (9).'

The uniform, both clothes and hair, became so established that it is almost what we think of first when we think of the poet whose collected works were published in 1908. It is most emphatically present, perhaps, in the formal photographs taken in the first years of the century (18, 19, 20). Beerbohm uses it in the famous cartoon – presumably to be dated about the turn of the century – where he seizes the absurd moment of George Moore's conversion to Yeats's Ireland (15). It helps William Strang to give some sort of identity to his academic drawings of 1903 (21, 22). It fixes the leading image for the 1908 portraits.

Beerbohm's Yeats was introducing Moore to faeryland; the classroom library contains not only *Erse without Tears* and *Murray's Guide to Ireland*, but *Half-Hours with the Symbols* and *Short Cuts to Mysticism*. This is Moore's Alick, the Yeats of the Golden Dawn and esoteric knowledge, the Yeats whom his mystical friend, W. T. Horton, caricatured in *The Academy* of the 8th July 1899 (16). The text calls this both a portrait and a criticism. Yeats is shown with the initiate's halo, an alchemist's retort, a magician's wand, books of magical formulae and a copy of William Blake (Beerbohm shows this too); he is the author of *Rosa Alchemica* and *The Secret Rose*. This is how he appeared, seriously, to that other symbolic artist Althea Gyles. In her drawing (17), intended as a frontispiece for *The Wind Among the Reeds*, Yeats is shown under the symbol of the Rose whose fourth detached petal drifts rather ambiguously before his face, illustrating perhaps these lines from 'To the Rose Upon the Rood of Time':

> 'Come near, come near, come near – Ah, leave me still
> A little space for the rose-breath to fill!'

9

Moore's Alick – his portrait was composed in the short period when Moore fancied they were in sympathy – is formidable. For any suggestion of the sombreness in Alick's face we must look at the photographs and not at the paintings and drawings. There is in Rolleston's snapshots (4, 5) or in the later posed studio portraits (18, 19, 20) a strength related to a certain heaviness of the lower face: a formation of mouth and jaw which John Butler Yeats carefully excluded, but which is visible in Sarah Purser's drawing (11) and even in Strang's; and which prepares us for the very remarkable photograph taken in 1908 by the young American photographer Alvin Langdon Coburn (24). This unpublished photograph may still be of the poet in his uniform, but it catches a note of something vivid that might well be formidable.

II   The second group of portraits is entirely connected with a given occasion: the publication of Yeats's *Collected Works* by A. H. Bullen at the Shakespeare Head Press in 1908. Yeats was now in his forty-third year and the publication of such an elaborate edition marked the establishment of his first reputation. He was rather sensitive about comments that might be made on the scale and apparent finality of such an edition, but this did not prevent him from devoting a great deal of attention – we can follow it in his letters – to the portraits that seemed an essential part of this presentation of himself; and he was quite determined to have what he wanted, though his original plan for having them all together 'for comparison and completeness' in one group, was not carried out. He refused to have a conventional photograph by one of the fashionable portrait photographers, and insisted on going to Alvin Langdon Coburn, the young American, 'who is celebrated in our world' – the London world, that is, of literature and the arts, notably the world of Ezra Pound, in which Coburn moved and was admired. But none of Coburn's photographs was used for this edition; and no photographs at all appear. Nor does the mask (27) done by Kathleen Bruce. Yeats also went to Charles Shannon. Shannon was the friend of Charles Ricketts: Yeats had known them since the late nineties, and Ricketts, his art and his views on art, were important for him. Shannon did a drawing which Yeats found 'very charming' but 'by an unlucky accident most damnably like Keats' and he decided that if he published it by itself everyone would think it an affectation. But Shannon also did a dull portrait – commissioned by John Quinn, the American patron – which was reproduced (26). Quinn, who collected Sargent, also commissioned a charcoal drawing from him, which Yeats reproduced in place of the Shannon drawing (34). Yeats also decided to use a pastel done by Mancini (25) whom Hugh Lane had taken up with great enthusiasm – more enthusiasm than judgement – and brought to Ireland. He would only have one of his father's drawings (9), which had already been seen as frontispiece to the 1897 *Tables of the Law*. Then there was Augustus John. He went to Coole in the summer of 1907; he climbed trees better than Robert Gregory; and Robert Gregory made him ride; and they all enjoyed themselves enormously. And John painted and drew Yeats many times in preparation for an etching wanted for the edition – but nothing by John was to be used. Only in the 1933 *Collected Poems* did one of the Coole portraits – that owned by Gogarty – appear, as frontispiece; and one of the etchings in the 1937 *Vision*.

Yeats was firm enough in his judgements: 'I have spent my life with pictures and was a painter for three years and I really think I might be trusted in this matter', he wrote angrily to Bullen. He would not have 'sentimental representations of myself alone.' So anything by his father had to be balanced with a less prejudiced version by another painter. Nor would he have John alone. He could find nothing to say of the Shannon except that 'it is not flattering' and is 'one of his grave distinguished old-masterish things.' He says nothing at all about Lady Kennet's mask – that un-individualised healthy open-air young man with only a suggestion of something myopic. He was very amused by Mancini (Lady Gregory quotes an entertaining account of his sitting in her *Hugh Lane*), but it is not likely that he was taken in by him or by his portrait 'of some dark-skinned café king in whom· I see a curious resemblance to myself,' although he described it to Bullen as 'a master work of one of the greatest living painters.' He is amused when he writes to Quinn:

> 'I am going to put the lot one after the other: my father's emaciated portrait that was the frontispiece for *The Tables of the Law* beside Mancini's brazen image, and Augustus John's tinker to black the nose of Shannon's idealist. Nobody will believe they are the same man. And I shall write an essay upon them and describe them as all different personages that I have dreamt of being but never had the time for.'

It is this rejection of John that is most interesting. 'A beautiful etching' he says 'and I understand what he means in it, and admire the meaning, but it is useless for my special purpose.' Yeats was clearly worried by John's portraits (28, 29, 30, 31, 32, 33). He insists that John has shown him as a gypsy, grown old in wickedness and hardship; the portraits are powerful, ugly, exaggerate every hollow and contour of the face. Yeats can find an ingenious interpretation: John has made him into a melancholy English Bohemian, 'capable of everything except living joyously on the surface.' Years later Yeats, in a diary written in 1930, was to recall how sharp the impression had been, in words that elaborate but corroborate his contemporary account.

> 'Always particular about my clothes, never dissipated, never unshaved except during illness, I saw myself there an unshaven, drunken bar-tender, and then I began to feel John had found something that he liked in me, something closer than character, and by that very transformation made it visible. He had found Anglo-Irish solitude, a solitude I have made for myself, an outlawed solitude.'

John tells in *Chiaroscuro* of how he found Yeats with his myopic eyes and hieratic gestures 'every inch a poet of the twilight.' Yet although he could certainly show Yeats as fragile (32) he could also show him as anything but fragile; and in the etchings Yeats is conspicuously unshaven, vigorous, and closer to Synge's world and his outlawed poets than to Coole Park. But if Yeats could recognise this as a version of the poet, this was not the poet he wished to stand in front of the volume of collected narrative and lyrical poems. He preferred to put Sargent's drawing there (34), at the entrance to the whole edition.

He called it 'a charming aerial sort of thing, very flattering as I think.' The charm and lightness contrasted, presumably, with John's power and ugliness. Sargent shows the romantic poet, face unlined, perpetually young – fixed for ever in his early twenties: never older than Keats – hair wild and eyes shadowed. The Coole portrait chosen for the 1933 and subsequent editions of the *Collected Poems* is the closest John came to this romantic image (35). The Sargent can still be seen in front of the *Collected Plays.*

III Between 1908 and 1930 we can find few portraits of Yeats. There is a group of drawings by William Rothenstein, of which we have traced only two, one in Dublin and one in Leeds (36, 37); and these seem to be noncommittal. There is also a head in bronze by Albert Power, commissioned by Gogarty and done in Dublin in early summer 1917

(38). It made him, Yeats thought, look 'rather humorous and intellectual than poetical': a just enough observation, and by 'poetical' Yeats probably still meant Sargent: iconography not having caught up with the fact. And there must be more photographs than we have succeeded in finding. We regret that we cannot record more fully the poet's metamorphosis into the 'sixty–year–old smiling public man.' The formal photographs (39, 40) taken about 1917 and in 1920 show the greying hair – Mrs Yeats recalls that in 1911 his hair was already brindled – and an unlined face that is very far from the Yeats of the 1924 group photograph (41).

This remarkable gathering – Yeats, Chesterton, James Stephens, Compton Mackenzie, Lennox Robinson, Augustus John – assembled in Dublin for the Tailteann Games (an ancient festival revived). Oliver St. John Gogarty seems to have been the impresario and the photograph was taken in his garden. It required, the story goes, some effort to persuade Yeats into the dress appropriate to a Senator. This Yeats we can easily imagine inspecting schools politely. He was indeed approaching his sixtieth year and the face had changed. When 'Mac' drew, in that same year probably, Yeats and Æ passing each other in Merrion Square, it is the fuller ageing face that he records, as well as this Merrion Square, Kildare Club and Senatorial phase of Yeats's life (42). And by now Yeats's hair was white and he was wearing the new costume, the coloured tweeds, the green or blue shirts, that had replaced the black uniform of the Twilight poet. As early as 1914 Max Beerbohm had observed, in an essay written in 1914 and broadcast in 1954:

> 'As years went by, the visual aspect of Yeats changed a little. His face grew gradually fuller in outline, and the sharp angles of his figure were smoothed away; and his hands – those hands which in his silences lay folded downward across his breast, but left each other and came forth, and as it were, stroked the air to and fro while he talked – those very long, fine hands did seem to have lost something of their insubstantiality. His dignity and his charms were as they had always been. But I found it less easy to draw caricatures of him. He seemed to have become subtly less like himself.'

Less like, that means, the poet of the 90s, the 'poetical' poet whom Yeats had missed in Power's bust. In 1930 at Renvyle, Gogarty's house in the west of Ireland, John found Yeats 'now a silver-haired old man, much mellowed and humanised' and painted him like this, a subdued humour in the pursed full mouth (43). And the notable

B

elegance of his old age, of hands, head, clothes and disposition of the body are caught four years later in Sean O'Sullivan's official portrait for the Abbey Theatre (44). But here, and both pose and expression catch it, there is tiredness and perhaps resignation. The fine modelling of the head and the appropriate hair are confirmed by the lucky snapshot taken about this time without his knowledge, at Lennox Robinson's house, Sorrento Cottage, Dalkey, by F. R. Higgins (45). A snapshot of 1935–1936 records, touchingly, the gentle fragility of illness and the friendship with the Swami Shri Purohit who showed him towards the end of his life, still eager after new things, yet further possibilities in the religious life (46).

The drama in Fleischmann's photograph may seem factitious (47); but a full statement of the poet's personality in his last great years seems to be offered by a remarkable group of photographs taken in 1937; and this is dramatic enough. The contrasts and connexions are instructive. On July 3rd 1937, Yeats introduced from London, a broadcast reading from his own poems. There are two photographs taken that day by a B.B.C. photographer (48, 49). Absorbed, tense, powerful, he is still the Yeats who had dominated audiences. Or, diverted and unposed, he is struck into another life, the gay and ribald old man who in the later poems so asserted his humanity. At the same time Howard Coster made a series of formal portraits. The last full representation of the poet and we might think the most memorable (50, 51, 52). The metamorphosis from the poet of the 1890s is now perfected. It is not easy to describe the personality revealed, except by saying that it seems now complete, and completely human; masculine, noble and nobly posed, and yet sardonic; assured and yet not deceived, having become exalted to the status of an image among images, a figure at last in his own poetry. Desmond MacCarthy said in an *Observer* obituary 'as he grew older, the dignity of his life and his impersonal pride as a poet lent a more enigmatic impressiveness to his romantic appearance.'

D. J. Gordon/Ian Fletcher

NOTES
1   Mrs W. B. Yeats's collection contains one drawing of W. B. Yeats as a small child asleep and one of 'Willie 1886', and one of him painting, 1870; another is in the National Library, Dublin.
2   *Letters to Katharine Tynan,* 1953, pp 93, 170. W B Y refers to a portrait by Walter Paget in this year. Both H. M. and Walter Paget were illustrators; both lived in Bedford Park.Connexions with H. M. were probably stronger. He lived next door to the Todhunters, and had a good deal to do with the production of *A Sicilian Idyll.* His wife, Etta, was a sister of Florence Farr. See p 174.

NOTE
In each catalogue list of material (apart from Books and Manuscripts) included in the Whitworth Art Gallery and Dublin exhibitions, the following methods of description are used:

Roman type for photographs only.
Bold type where the object itself is shown as well as the photograph.
Italics throughout for paintings, prints, drawings and other works which do not appear in the photographic record.
*Pictures shown at the Whitworth Art Gallery but not at Dublin.

1 **W. B. Yeats by J. B. Yeats, 1886; pen drawing in the collection of Mrs W. B. Yeats.**
2 **W. B. Yeats by H. M. Paget, 1889; oil painting in the Belfast Art Gallery.**
3 W. B. Yeats, photograph by Lafayette, 1894; Mrs W. B. Yeats' collection. (Pl. 1)
4 W. B. Yeats, photograph by T. W. Rolleston, 1894; negative in Lady Albery's possession; published by C. H. Rolleston, *Portrait of an Irishman,* London, 1939.
5 W. B. Yeats, photograph by T. W. Rolleston, 1894; negative in Lady Albery's possession.
6 Richard Le Gallienne 1897, photographed from R. Whittington-Egan and G. Smerdon, *The Quest of the Golden Boy,* London, 1960.
7 W. B. Yeats by J. B. Yeats, c1894; pencil drawing formerly in the collection of Lennox Robinson; reproduced in *Autobiographies,* ed. 1955.
8 **W. B. Yeats by J. B. Yeats, probably 1890's; oil painting in the Municipal Gallery, Dublin.**
9 W. B. Yeats by J. B. Yeats, November 1896; pencil drawing, whereabouts unknown; reproduced in: *Literary Year Book,* 1897; *Tables of the Law,* frontispiece, 1897; *Collected Works,* 1908, VII, frontispiece.

10 **W. B. Yeats by J. B. Yeats, 8th December 1897; pencil drawing in the collection of Mrs W. B. Yeats.**

11 **W. B. Yeats by Sarah Purser; pastel drawing, in the Municipal Gallery, Dublin.**

12 **W. B. Yeats by J. B. Yeats 1898; watercolour in the National Gallery of Ireland, Dublin.**

13 **W. B. Yeats by J. B. Yeats, 28th January 1899; pencil drawing in the collection of Mrs W. B. Yeats.**

14 **W. B. Yeats by J. B. Yeats, 1900; oil painting in the National Gallery of Ireland, Dublin; another oil by J. B. Yeats, formerly in the collection of Mrs. W. B. Yeats, is now in the Wardroom Mess, Royal Naval Barracks, Haulbowline; v** *T C D Cat.* **No. 155.**

15 'Mr W. B. Yeats presenting Mr George Moore to the Queen of the Fairies' by Max Beerbohm; watercolour in the Municipal Gallery, Dublin; published in *The Poet's Corner,* 1904.

16 W. B. Yeats by W. T. Horton; caricature drawing reproduced in *The Academy,* 8th July, 1899.

17 W. B. Yeats by Althea Gyles, c1900; pen drawing in the British Museum; intended as a frontispiece for *The Wind among the Reeds.*

18 W. B. Yeats, photograph c1902; from print in Mrs C. MacBride's collection.

19 W. B. Yeats, photograph c1902; from print in Mrs W. B. Yeats' collection. (Pl. 2).

20 W. B. Yeats, photograph c1902; from the Radio Times, Hulton Library.

21 *****W. B. Yeats by William Strang, c1903; black, white and red chalk drawing in the Fitzwilliam Museum, Cambridge.**

22 W. B. Yeats by William Strang, 1903; chalk drawing in the National Gallery of Ireland, Dublin.

23 **W. B. Yeats by J. B. Yeats, 20th March 1904; pencil drawing in the collection of Mrs W. B. Yeats.**

24 W. B. Yeats, photograph by Alvin Langdon Coburn, Dublin, 24th January 1908; another version is reproduced in *Poems, Second Series,* 1909; print by Alvin Langdon Coburn. (Pl. 3).

24a W. B. Yeats reciting a poem, photograph by Alvin Langdon Coburn, Dublin, 24th January 1908.'

25 *W. B. Yeats by A. Mancini, October 1907; pastel drawing in the collection of Mrs W. B. Yeats; reproduced in Collected Works, 1908, V, frontispiece.*

26 W. B. Yeats by Charles Shannon, oil painting, commissioned by John Quinn, but present whereabouts unknown; reproduced in *Collected Works,* 1908, III, frontispiece.

27 W. B. Yeats by Kathleen Bruce (Lady Kennet), 1908; plaster mask, bronzed, in the National Portrait Gallery, London.

28 **Studies of W. B. Yeats by Augustus John, 1907; pencil drawing in the Tate Gallery; another sheet of drawings is reproduced in Lillian Browse,** *Augustus John Drawings,* **1946, 12, pl.12. (Pl. 5).**

29 and 30 *W. B. Yeats, etchings by Augustus John; the etching exists in five versions; see Campbell Dodgson, 'A Catalogue of Etchings by John', 1920. These are Dodgson's 1 and 5; in the collection of the University of Reading.*

31 **W. B. Yeats by Augustus John, 1907; oil painting in the Manchester City Art Gallery (formerly in Lady Gregory's collection).**

32 **W. B. Yeats by Augustus John, 1907; oil painting in the Tate Gallery; another version in monochrome, reproduced** *Coll. Poems,* **1933, and later, v.** *T C D Cat.* **No. 156, in the collection of Arthur Cox, Esq. A bust done by Augustus John after the 1907 portraits, is now in the possession of the Abbey Theatre.** (Pl. 4).

33 *W. B. Yeats by Augustus John, 1907; pen and wash drawing in the National Portrait Gallery, London.*

34 W. B. Yeats by J. S. Sargent; charcoal drawing commissioned by John Quinn, but present whereabouts unknown.

35 *W. B. Yeats by Augustus John, 1908; oil painting in the collection of Arthur Cox, Esq.*

36 **W. B. Yeats by Sir William Rothenstein, 1916; pencil drawing in the Leeds City Art Gallery.**

37 *W. B. Yeats by Sir William Rothenstein, 1916; pencil drawing in the Municipal Gallery, Dublin.*

38 W. B. Yeats by Albert Power, commissioned by Gogarty, 1917; bronze head in the collection of Arthur Cox, Esq.

39 W. B. Yeats, photograph by G. Toplis, 27 Stanwick Road, London, c1917; in the collection of Mrs W. B. Yeats.

40 W. B. Yeats, photograph by Underwood and Underwood, 417 Fifth Avenue, New York, 1920; in the collection of Mrs W. B. Yeats.

41 W. B. Yeats with Chesterton, James Stephens, Compton Mackenzie, Lennox Robinson, and Augustus John; photographed in Gogarty's garden at Dublin, 1924; Lennox Robinson collection.

42 *'Chin-Angles or How the Poets Passed' by S. M. Macnie (Mac), c1925; from a print in Lennox Robinson's collection.*

43 **W. B. Yeats by Augustus John, 1930; oil painting in the Glasgow City Art Gallery. (Pl. 6).**

44 **W. B. Yeats by Sean O'Sullivan, 1934; oil painting in the collection of the Abbey Theatre, Dublin; a study for this portrait, and a head in pastel, by the same artist are in the collection of the late John L. Birke, Esq.**

45 W. B. Yeats, photographed at Sorrento Cottage, Dalkey by F. R. Higgins, c1930.

46 W. B. Yeats and Shri Purohit, photographed during visit to Majorca and Spain, 1935/6; from a print in the collection of Gerald Yorke, Esq.

47 W. B. Yeats, photograph by Fleischmann, c1935; Mrs W. B. Yeats' collection.

48 W. B. Yeats, photographed by the B.B.C. on the occasion of his broadcast, 3rd July 1937. (Frontispiece).

49 W. B. Yeats, photographed by the B.B.C. on the occasion of his broadcast, 3rd July 1937.

50 W. B. Yeats, photograph by Howard Coster, 1937.

51 W. B. Yeats, photograph by Howard Coster, 1937.

52 W. B. Yeats, photograph by Howard Coster, 1937.

3   W. B. Yeats, 1894

Plate 1

19   W. B. Yeats, c.1902

Plate 2

Plate 3

32　*W. B. Yeats*
　　by Augustus John, 1907
　　Courtesy of the Tate Gallery

Plate 4

28 *W. B. Yeats*
    by Augustus John, 1907
    Courtesy of the Tate Gallery

Plate 5

43 *W. B. Yeats*
by Augustus John, 1930
Courtesy of the Glasgow Museums and Art Galleries

Plate 6

PERSONS AND PLACES

'. . . an Ireland
The poets have imagined, terrible and gay. '

For Yeats, nature and experience were a book of images. Places and persons that had most deeply moved him took on a further dimension of meaning. Through physical appearance, historical association, act or gesture, they could become, if only for a moment, epiphanies of a truth beyond the limits of the accident that is Ben Bulben, Coole Park or Lissadell, Robert Gregory's 'lonely death', or Constance Markiewicz's part in the Irish struggle for independence. This we have tried to illustrate: not his biography, or the history of modern Ireland.

I   THOOR BALLYLEE

' I declare this tower to be my symbol. '

Our first group of photographs, with Robert Gregory's sepia drawing (53, 54, 55, 56, 57, 58, 59) shows Thoor Ballylee in Galway, and its landscapes. Yeats bought this Anglo-Norman tower, which had belonged to the Gregory estate, in 1917, and for some years spent part of the summer there with his family. He had known the Tower since his early visits to Coole and apart from the need he felt for a house of his own in the country, it was an admirably apt personal symbol. He had always seen himself as one in a line of solitary searchers after a hidden wisdom, like Milton's Platonist, Shelley's Prince Athanase, or Villiers de l'Isle Adam's Count Axël, for each of whom the tower had been a symbol of solitude and search and the mind's introspection. Samuel Palmer's etching of the Penseroso's 'Lonely Tower' (283) was the perfect illustration of this image.

'He has found, after the manner of his kind,
Mere images; chosen this place to live in
Because, it may be, of the candle-light
From the far tower where Milton's Platonist
Sat late, or Shelley's visionary prince:
The lonely light that Samuel Palmer engraved,
An image of mysterious wisdom won by toil. . . .'

The Tower itself could stand for the poet's pride and isolation, its winding stair for the gyres of history or the way of purgatory. Thus it fulfils the requirements of the perfect symbol, for it also visibly exists and has a physical history: its walls, inhabited and desolate, and built again, hold the cycles of history.

Thoor Ballylee, one of a number of such towers in Galway, built of the grey local stone, stands by an ancient fording place on an island site, enclosed by the fast-flowing stream and a backwater. It has four storeys, each of a single room, and a flat and battlemented roof. Close under it on the landward side is a cottage and a walled garden. Tower, cottage and garden were all reconstructed. The shallow river valley is lightly wooded and from the battlements you look across to the thickly wooded demesne of Coole and the severe and stony out-line of the Burren hills. The hamlet of Ballylee was the home of the blind poet Raftery, and of Mary Hynes, the peasant Helen, both of whom Yeats celebrated in *The Tower.* Mary Hynes lived in a poem by Raftery as both now live in Yeats's poem, and his knowledge of both goes back to the days when Lady Gregory was collecting lore and traditions around Coole, at the turn of the century. Through her work and Douglas Hyde's, Raftery was established as the last great name in the native tradition of the wandering bard, poet of the folk: a tradition linking heroic Ireland with the blind rhapsode who sang in Greece. On the wall facing the road are placed the lines that Yeats – 'I the poet, William Yeats' – wrote to commemorate his work of reconstruction, praying that

'. . . these characters remain
When all is ruin once again. '

The ruin has been accomplished with an almost too dramatic appro-priateness; the cottage is now roofless; the garden overgrown with huge weeds; the tower roof leaks; graffiti are scribbled on the wall and window embrasure; rooms have been stripped of woodwork, and a plank has even been torn from the great oak door.

26

II COOLE PARK AND LADY GREGORY

' A moment's memory to that laurelled head. '

The second group of photographs shows the empty site of Coole Park, Galway, among its woods; its avenue of over-arching elm and ilex, the vestiges of its formal garden. Coole was an unpretentious eighteenth century mansion (60, 61, 62). When Yeats first knew it, it was the home of Lady Gregory (1852–1932) widow of Sir William, whom she had married in his old age, with whom she had moved in the great houses of London, at the centre of imperial diplomacy and politics. The land of Galway is poor and Coole's beauty lay in its lake and its great woods, for Sir William had inherited a passion for planting, and for rare species. When Yeats first met Augusta Gregory in 1896, she was forty-four years of age and the editor of her husband's autobiography and his grandfather's correspondence. She was interested in the Irish language, and in sympathy with Irish nationalism, and as always, assiduous in her local charities. At the time of Yeats's first long visit to Coole in 1897, he was in a state of virtual collapse, both physical and emotional, the effect of long years of hackwork and poverty, combined with the stress of his restless intellectual hunger and his failure in love. Lady Gregory, that summer, nursed him back into health and for very many years Coole was in fact his home: 'my home for nearly forty years.' It is easy to smile faintly and shrug the shoulders at Lady Gregory's relationship with Yeats: the eggs beaten in wine; the clean blotting pad on the desk every morning; the careful regimen of hours of work and hours of walking and fishing and relaxation that she prescribed for him. But Yeats himself knew how much he owed to her. She played a decisive role in his life, and for good; and their association lasted until her death, though its significance changed with time. Through Yeats she was led to play an active part in the Irish Literary Movement, by the preparation of versions of the heroic literature, in the collection of folk-lore, nourishment for Yeats's own studies, and most conspicuously in the creation of an Irish drama and a national theatre. From her association with Yeats, Lady Gregory also gained a sense of direction in her life and in her fifties began to produce a series of vivid, fantasticated comedies and tragicomedies. In her old age she knew much trouble and long and painful infirmity:

'Sound of a stick upon the floor, a sound
From somebody that toils from chair to chair.'

Her nephew, Hugh Lane, was drowned in the *Lusitania* in 1915; her indefatigable efforts to secure the return of the Lane pictures to

Dublin proved unsuccessful; her only child, Robert Gregory, was killed in action in 1918; and her years of struggle to maintain the estate ended in 1927 when she had to sell both land and house to a Government department, which bought for the sake of the trees. All this she met with the same fortitude. Within some years of her death, Coole was pulled down. What a forester will show the infrequent visitor are a fragment of the broken walls of the dairy and the ruins of the early 19th century stables. A hundred yards or so from the house are the sad remains, set in deep woods, of the formal garden where the yew alleys and the catalpa rise from the long grass (63, 64, 65, 66). It is the ruin that Yeats foresaw.

> 'When all those rooms and passages are gone,
> When nettles wave upon a shapeless mound
> And saplings root among the broken stone. . . .'

What local piety has preserved is the great tree, where – an affecting piece of almost Victorian ritual – Lady Gregory's famous guests were led to carve their initials.

No one has raised a monument to Lady Gregory at Coole. Her books are little read; her plays rarely performed. There was certainly that in her personality which provoked the defence of laughter, but never in her presence. They will tell you in Gort that she is remembered because in the bad times the women were always allowed to gather sticks in the woods and for her kindness to the children of her tenants. In Yeats, Augusta Gregory and her house moved affection and gratitude, a willingly paid debt; more than this, in her life and more poignantly as her death approached, she and her house appeared as emblematic of values he saw threatened and an effort lost. Coole (67) was Lady Gregory and Douglas Hyde and Synge and Raftery: noble, scholar, poet: the great tradition.

> 'We were the last romantics – chose for theme
> Traditional sanctity and loveliness;
> Whatever's written in what poets name
> The book of the people. . . .'

Raftery was the poet who used that phrase; looking at Coole now, Yeats sees that Homer's horse is riderless, that their shared dream and sole test – 'dream of the noble and the beggar-man' – belonged to a past that had gone like Coole. And Coole embodied order, ceremony, freedom and humility:

> 'All that pride and that humility. . . .'

Proper pride, proper humility and freedom are only possible for aristocrat, artist and beggar, because they are free from the tyranny of prudential wisdom and the timidities of the bourgeois. Only from this freedom can issue the great gesture, which may be act or vision or work of art, the sign of that human completeness which John Butler Yeats called 'personality'.

In a letter, Yeats records that someone, from whom such feelings might not have been expected, walked from room to room in Coole, the day after Lady Gregory's death, and after standing silent under the portraits said 'all the nobility of earth.' 'I felt', wrote Yeats, 'he did not mean it for that room alone but for the lost tradition. How much of my own verse has not been but the repetition of those words' (68).

Lady Gregory liked Mancini's portrait of her which Hugh Lane had commissioned about 1906 (69); a 'radiant transfiguration' she called it, and in the account of her sittings in her *Life* of Hugh Lane – and of Mancini's manipulations of his fish-net – wrote 'at the end his portrait of a woman growing old and a dusty black dress, and a faded brown curtain would have lighted up a prison cell'. Synge, not often enthusiastic, spoke of it as 'the greatest portrait since Rembrandt'. Yeats quoted this in *The Municipal Gallery Revisited,* but his rider–'a great ebullient portrait certainly'–seems to indicate some reserve. The portraits by J. B. Yeats (70), Flora Lion (71), Æ and Gerald Kelly seem to show little but the gently-born Victorian widow. Only the 1911 photograph by her niece Ruth Shine (72) and the 1910 bust by Epstein, seem to show something of the quality that must have been hers; and these dates are to be noted, for that was the time of the *Playboy* controversy and the struggle for Lane's gallery, and Yeats's poems about her in *The Green Helmet* and *Responsibilities.*

Hugh Lane, who commissioned it, did not like the Epstein, and thought it did not go with the marbles at Coole Park; Lady Gregory's own attitude was equivocal. She remembered that during one sitting she fell into animated conversation about the theatre with some chance visitor, and forgot the artist until she found that 'pleased with some gesture, he had cut through the clay throat, tilting head and chin in an eternal eagerness.' She suggests that the bust balances the Mancini, as though 'by some star less magnificent than Jupiter, Epstein had been beckoned in as Devil's Advocate'. But its closeness to the photograph is clear; and some found in it her best likeness. It is a formidable head (73, 74).

c

Robert Gregory (1881-1918) was Augusta Gregory's only child. In 1899 he went up from Harrow to New College where he took a third in Moderations in 1901 and a third in Greats in 1903. Before he went down from Oxford he had already begun to design and paint sets for the productions of the new Irish plays; and on leaving Oxford he studied painting at the Slade School. In 1907 he married a fellow student and from about 1909 he spent some periods at Jacques Emile Blanche's atelier *La Palette* in Paris: Blanche had long-standing English connexions and his modified and by now traditional version of Impressionism appealed to young men from England who were not in sympathy with the Academy but did not wish to immerse themselves in the latest avant-garde movements. Much of Gregory's life, however, after his marriage, was spent at Coole Park, where his mother still lived, and effectively managed the estate. In October 1914 he had an exhibition of his paintings at the Chenil Gallery in Chelsea. He joined the army in 1915 as a Second Lieutenant in the 4th Connaught Rangers. 'I joined up out of friendship' he told Yeats. Next year, in January, he transferred to the Royal Flying Corps; later in that same year he was promoted to the rank of Temporary Captain. On June 26th 1917, he became *Chevalier* of the *Légion d' Honneur.* In July of that same year he was promoted Temporary Major. The following citation appears in *The London Gazette* for 18th July 1917, on the award to him of the Military Cross:

> 'For conspicuous gallantry and devotion to duty. On many occasions he has, at various altitudes, attacked and destroyed or driven down hostile machines and has invariably displayed the highest courage and skill.'

On January 23rd, he was killed in action on the North Italian front: shot down in error – according to the official records of the Royal Flying Corps – by an Italian pilot. Neither his family nor Yeats knew this.

Yeats wrote four poems on Robert Gregory: *The Sad Shepherd* (later known as *Shepherd and Goatherd),* a pastoral elegy in the manner of Spencer; *In Memory of Major Robert Gregory; An Irish Airman Foresees His Death;* and *Reprisals,* a short bitter poem provoked by the actions of the Black and Tans at Coole, published posthumously, as Yeats felt that its suggestion that her son's death was valueless would wound Lady Gregory. He also contributed an 'appreciation' of Gregory to the *Observer,* for Sunday, 17th February 1918.

Of Gregory's friends most of those, perhaps, who knew him best are dead. We work with sparse and broken recollections, often conveyed at second hand; we are made to realise again the line that the 1914/18 war drew across the lives we meet: friendships and social groupings were broken; recollections are almost of another world and other selves. Gregory remains elusive. He was charming, handsome, blond, shorter perhaps than we imagine him – friendly, unassuming, quiet, if anything withdrawn. That he was eminently gifted as an athlete – particularly as a horseman – there is no doubt; and his versatility was striking. The tale of his accomplishments may be given in a prose very unlike Yeats's appreciation: language recalling an age and tone quite gone, with an effect that is curiously touching, like the dim, badly reproduced little photograph that goes with it: that conventional First War photograph of the young officer in uniform that we all remember seeing on tables or in albums in our childhood. This is from the *Illustrated Sporting and Dramatic News* of 23rd February 1918:

> 'After leaving college he studied art at the Slade and under Blanche in Paris, and as an artist attracted considerable attention. He was also an all-round sportsman. A good shot, a fine boxer, an excellent slow-break bowler, and a fearless horseman and point-to-point rider. He belonged to the Authentic Co. Galway, and Phoenix Cricket Clubs, and got eight of the wickets for the Gentlemen of Ireland v Scotland match the last time he played in Dublin. At Oxford he was chosen as light-weight boxer against Cambridge, and in Paris as a candidate for the amateur championship of France. One of the leading members of the 'Galway Blazers' writes: 'A gallant fellow, one of the very best, I don't suppose he knew what fear was, for a more fearless horseman never rode over this country'. Major Gregory evidently carried these qualities from the hunting field to the fighting line, whence his Colonel wrote: 'his skill and courage were superlative', and one of his Flight Commanders adds 'A really fine airman, and a dead game man'.

It is this Gregory who stands with the rest of the Phoenix Cricket Club team in a group photograph of about 1908 (75).

Of Gregory's gifts as painter and designer there is less certainty. What he actually accomplished we do not know very much about; his pictures, if they have been preserved, are not collected: odd examples only can be found. What he might have done we cannot guess. Augustus John, who remembers Gregory, praises his work for conveying something of the strange quality of the Galway landscape, adding emphatically: 'He had talent'. 'Yes, but not enough', responds another friend, an accomplished woman who had seen much of the Coole Park circle. Henry Lamb, who met Gregory while they were both at Blanche's, remembered their early morning rides in Paris more vividly than Gregory's work; and also his surprise that Gregory, so much a sportsman, so much in appearance and bearing the type of the soldier, should be in that milieu of artists; and his doubts about whether Gregory would ever go very far with his painting; and remembered, too, a notable uncertainty of performance. One old friend blamed Lady Gregory for distracting him from serious painting by making him design sets and paint scenes. Yet another thinks that it was in this field that Gregory might have worked best. His mother hoped very early that her son might prove to be a distinguished painter. And it is certainly not by accident that in the portrait which she commissioned from Shannon in 1906 he should be shown, formally, as painter (76). Whether his mother's hopes were a stimulus to him, or a burden, we do not know. There is agreement that he did not devote himself to painting with a singleness of purpose, except perhaps in the few years just before the war when he seemed to work more assiduously and systematically. The 1914 exhibition may have been a decisive declaration of an ambition. Yet even so, a reviewer in *The Studio*, October 1914, remarked that 'this artist's drawing lacks assurance even in its own vein'. 'An uneasy man': this is the phrase that Henry Lamb used to sum up his memory of Gregory.

Such uncertainties about the direction of Gregory's talent and his future underlie the grave elaborations of Yeats's beautiful 'appreciation'. Yeats is concerned to establish as well as to mourn. 'His very accomplishment hid from many his genius. He had so many sides . . . that some among his friends were not sure what his work would be. To me he will always remain a great painter in the immaturity of his youth, he himself the personification of handsome youth. . . . Though he often seemed led away from his work by some other gift, his attitude to life and art never lost intensity – he was never the amateur . . . his constant struggle to resist those other gifts that brought him ease and friendship'. Gregory was thirty-seven when he was killed. He had told Bernard Shaw, Yeats recalls, that the months since he joined the army had been the happiest of his life, and goes on, 'I think they brought him peace of mind, an escape from that shrinking, which I sometimes saw upon his face, before the growing absorption of his dream'.

In life, Gregory's versatility, his ability to touch so many sides of it, may have been a doubtful gift, of uncertain issue. To art it gave an image. 'Soldier, scholar, horseman he', wrote Yeats in his elegy and 'Our Sidney and our perfect man'. Yeats offers Gregory as 'the many-sided man', located in history and in a living tradition.

Scholars had found this to be the human type aspired to and realised, after Italian precept and model, in the Renaissance. Sidney, poet and scholar, who died young in a trivial battle, making his gesture, figured familiarly as the English realisation of that type. The text-book was Castiglione's *Courtier,* which Lady Gregory had read aloud to Yeats during a summer at Coole. Castiglione's Urbino and Guidobaldo's court are the ideal city which Yeats had set against Dublin, a 'grammar school of courtesies' against Paudeen's town; an aristocracy against the middle classes; and it was when he was with Lady Gregory and Robert Gregory in North Italy that he chose to go to Urbino. When Lady Gregory almost died in 1909 he wrote: 'All Wednesday I heard Castiglione's phrase ringing in my memory, "Never be it spoken without tears, the Duchess, too, is dead" '. The complex of relationships is clearly established; and the elegy takes its place as a handling of one of Yeats's persisting themes. For the Gregory of the poem, sharp and early death was the only imaginable end – 'What made us dream that he could comb grey hair?' The revelation of complete mastery is the sharp flare: consummation that is extinction; extinction that is a condition of triumph. Gregory's mastery was that of 'Renaissance Man'. A mastery that last could live and flourish in Europe between the middle of the fifteenth century and the beginning of the seventeenth. So Yeats had come to believe as he meditated on 'unity of being' (an idea whose sources are complex but include nineteenth-century interpretations of the Renaissance as well as his father's speculations on 'character' and 'personality') and its relationship to the cycles of history. For a moment Gregory had been what he was. His triumph was alien and impossible to the modern world. In the 'subjective' phase in which the modern world stands, painter or poet – Yeats identifies their disciplines in the poem through a passage he has remembered from Palmer – is no longer in harmony with himself, his society and the world outside him. Art, that should be the means of communication, has become a means of isolation; for now to create art the artist must embrace in solitude a dream. Gregory, in peace, would have had to make the choice, or to refuse it. War – always in Yeats's interpretation – saved him, and, liberating him from the necessity, made him happy:

'I think they brought him peace of mind, an escape from that shrinking, which I sometimes saw upon his face, before the growing absorption of his dream, as from his constant struggle

to resist those other gifts that brought him ease and friendship.
Leading his squadron in France or in Italy, mind and hand
were at one, will and desire.'

Art, the poem, knows nothing of such shrinkings, such doubts:
only that the work, the impossible triumph of being life's epitome,
is accomplished in that flare.

IV LIONEL JOHNSON, J. M. SYNGE AND GEORGE POLLEXFEN

In this same poem, *In Memory of Major Robert Gregory,* Yeats
introduces three other figures, who had played a considerable part
in his life either through personal attachment or through their effect
on his imagination: Lionel Johnson (1867–1902), J. M. Synge (1871–
1909) and George Pollexfen (1840-1910).

In 1898, Yeats wrote of Johnson that he had chosen to live in solitude, like Axel in his tower, between two dreams: of Ireland and
the Catholic Church. Johnson was still alive when Yeats so
mythologized him; but, as Yeats knew, he was already a dead man.
His life had entered that 'mythic' phase, as another contemporary
called it, a living death of illness, terror, remorse, whisky and
isolation. There is little distance between biography and Yeats's
account of Johnson in his prose.

Associated with and distinguished from Gregory by his remote
scholarship and distant courtesy, Johnson is a type of the solitary
artist unable to accept the burden of that solitude and unable also
to accept absorption into the dream that creates solitude. Sanctity
is impossible: for hearts full of the image can have no place for the
Hound of Heaven. The saint must be out of passion, but the artist
cannot evade it. To Johnson, religion could bring torment only,
not peace. A classical Augustinian Christian, he told Yeats that he
found those who denied the eternity of punishment insufferably
vulgar. The strain of belief in this doctrine we can gather from his
Dark Angel, where Johnson veers first towards materialism: no soul,
no punishment:

> 'Less dread a change to drifting dust
> Than thine eternity of cares. . . .'

then towards a transcendentalism that would take the painful
tensions out of Christian belief:

'Do what thou will, thou shalt not so
Dark Angel, triumph over me.
Lonely to the lone, I go:
Divine to the Divinity.'

These are the words of Plotinus, not St. Paul. The alone that flies to the alone is not a complex human person, but a disembodied spirit that has lost the pain of its identity.

Johnson turned night into day, he studied and drank in solitude. His life was not unified by the sequence of ordinary human passions: romantic love, family responsibility, worldly ambition. Yet, as Yeats records, he unconsciously desired the world he had renounced. He attempted to graft his life on to the impersonal life of institutions: Winchester, Oxford, the Catholic Church, Ireland. His classical and patristic learning – he was intended to be the theologian of the Literary Movement – fed his imagination with a dream of a Celtic and Christian Ireland – a learned Ireland of the Saints – that had no relevance to the Catholic Ireland of the present. 'Much falling' morally and physically, Johnson was indeed the embodiment of Mallarmé's *chute,* of an age when imagination and learning, myth and fact were widely divergent. And Johnson's apocalyptic quest is, like Childe Roland's, sustained and impressive, but also enigmatic, even meaningless. Unlike Gregory's, Johnson's death is slow—matter of pathos; yet the sonority of that 'measureless consummation' suggests also that his defeat is not without nobility.

Johnson refused to sit for Rothenstein; by now he probably hated himself too much. It is right that the only photographs we have been able to find should date from his Winchester days, and that one should be a school group (77, 78, 79). The elegant, equivocal, blond head stands out. And the reports agree that the tiny body and the schoolboy's face did not change. If this is a sinister sign, then Johnson was marked.

The work and fate of few of his contemporaries impressed Yeats more deeply than Synge's; and Yeats recalled few episodes in his life with more pleasure than that first meeting with Synge in the Left Bank hotel in 1896, when he advised the young man to give up his desultory attempts at critical journalism and 'go to the Aran Islands and find a life that had never been expressed in literature, instead of a life where all had been expressed'. Synge and his work in Ireland affected Yeats's own life and work, and meditation on Synge came to be a meditation on the nature of the artist and what happens to him in the modern world. Yeats's protracted and violent defence of Synge's work was a strong element in his growing sense of his own estrangement from the life and feelings of Dublin. (*Estrangement* is the title Yeats chose when he came to publish his reflections on the death of Synge). Ireland's quarrel with Synge and the lengths to which his enemies were prepared to go dramatised the world's quarrel with the artist.

When later Yeats came to elaborate his theory of personality in relation to phases of history, he came to see Synge and his failure to communicate as exemplary of a certain case. This is the case of the artist whose only possible salvation lay in the flight from the subjective, 'all that subjective dreaming, that had once been power and joy, now corrupting within him. He had to take the first plunge into the world beyond himself'. And this is what the Aran Islands were for Synge, and what that society did for him. His isolation was matched by the isolation of that society; refusing the modern world, he could find in those islands a world remote as himself and full of passion and extravagance, a life that had not been 'expressed by literature' and a language that was not exhausted. So his most private images were given life and substance. From dreams, Lionel Johnson could escape only to still more impossible dreams. Synge escaped by celebrating the objective, a life antithetical to his own. Solitary, and a dying man, he wrote of life at its highest pitch of comic exuberance or harsh tragedy:

> '. . . dying chose the living world for text
> And never could have rested in the tomb
> But that, long travelling, he had come
> Towards nightfall upon certain set apart
> In a most desolate stony place,
> Towards nightfall upon a race
> Passionate and simple like his heart.'

'He was too timid, too shy for general conversation, an invalid and full of moral scruple, and he was to create now some ranting braggadocio, now some tipsy hag full of poetical speech, and now some young man or girl full of the most abounding health. He never spoke an unkind word, had admirable manners, and yet his art was to fill the streets with rioters, and to bring upon his dearest friends enemies that may last their lifetime.' It is the paradox that Yeats would emphasise in prose and poem: the tension between subjective and objective, isolation and communication, artist and society. The best known portrait of Synge is J. B. Yeats's oil in the Municipal

Gallery, Dublin (80): 'the grave deep face', Yeats said of it. This is just; and is apparent in all J. B. Yeats's portrait drawings (81): but the gravity is checked by the lively eyes. Very strange is Robert Gregory's drawing of 1904 where the eyes are closed: it looks like a death mask (82).

The third of the contrasting figures is George Pollexfen, Yeats's maternal uncle and one of his father's early and intimate friends. Yeats, to whom he was deeply attached and of whom he was very proud, spent much time with him and his housekeeper, Mary Battle, in their isolated cottages just outside Sligo or at Rosses Point on the sea. As a young man Pollexfen had been, like Gregory, a splendid horseman; it is this aspect of him that J. B. Yeats's romantic drawing shows (83). However in later years he gave up riding altogether. He withdrew more and more into an entirely secluded and private life, rarely stirring from Sligo, afflicted increasingly by melancholia and hypochondria:

> 'And Masons drove from miles away
> To scatter the Acacia spray
> Upon a melancholy man
> Who had ended where his breath began.'

His housekeeper had the second sight; and he himself became increasingly concerned with the unseen world; and under Yeats's tutelage he joined in experiments in the evocation of visions by the use of symbols; and became a member of the Order of the Golden Dawn. Astrology came to occupy him most and he became expert in the casting of horoscopes.

Pollexfen was not an artist. But his life resembled at certain important points those of Johnson and Synge, and contrasted with Gregory's. Here is a man who ceased to be able to communicate with his fellows, although he possessed particularly obvious and acceptable gifts, his riding and his knowledge of horses. He abandoned the life of communication and action for the dream of astrology. Not that Yeats believed astrology to be a silly dream; but he is concerned in the poem to make contrast between the world shown by the stars and the world of 'meets and racecourses' and 'solid men' to which his uncle had belonged, as our formal photograph of him in riding clothes most clearly shows (84). To this world the stars are said to be 'outrageous'. Between the two worlds there was an absolute split. His choice of the stars paralysed Pollexfen, and he became inert in melancholy.

'What could have made her peaceful with a mind
That nobleness made simple as a fire,
With beauty like a tightened bow, a kind
That is not natural in an age like this,
Being high and solitary and most stern?
Why, what could she have done, being what she is?
Was there another Troy for her to burn?'

Yeats met Maud Gonne in 1889. She was famous then, and became increasingly so for her beauty and her remarkable gifts as speaker and agitator. Her beauty is a legend among those who are still alive: but except for her commanding height, we have singularly little description of her appearance in youth, and the photographs and portrait we show convey little of the quality of that beauty. Neither painter nor photographer helps us to realise the effect she made (85, 86, 87, 88). She is indeed obviously beautiful, the outlines and modelling of the face are noble, and the eyes are fine: but it is a studio, post-card beauty, except that once under a large hat, the eyes have something more than the obligatory wistfulness. Clearly hers was a beauty of total impression: *et vera incessu patuit dea.* Yeats fell in love with her soon after their first meeting. She would never marry him and he could not eventually approve of her political activities, yet neither seemed willing to let the other go. It was only after many years of pain and frustration that he escaped from the prison of this incomplete relationship. She haunted his poetry from the moment they met till the end of his life. She appears under many guises: she is the Rose of the early poems, she is Deirdre, and perhaps principally, Helen, 'the Ledaean Body'. No woman's beauty has been so splendidly and continuously celebrated in modern poetry, from the moment when Yeats saw her at Bedford Park in his father's house, with the light falling through a great heap of apple blossoms by her side, to the moment when in his and her old age her sculptured image – and indeed her very face had by now taken on the monumental qualities of sculpture – recalled that beauty's danger and its terror. In his middle period as he grew more disillusioned with practical political energies, and as she persisted in what seemed to him increasingly random agitation, she had come to represent in his verse some of the things he hated most. Her politics he now saw as an abstraction imposed on the reality of life. For her, reality should have lain in the beauty that she seemed to hate, and attempted to destroy. Woman's beauty for Yeats was mysterious and should be inexpressive: it came from within and could be withered by the search for abstraction in any form. But it is precisely in her old age, even in the plaster bust (89), done when she was sixty-six, and notably in Horvath's spectacularly beautiful photograph, taken when she was in her eighties, that we can see the fascination and power (90):

> 'Hollow of cheek as though it drank the wind
> And took a mess of shadows for its meat.'

VI JOHN O'LEARY AND JOHN BUTLER YEATS

'Beautiful lofty things: O'Leary's noble head' is the opening line of a poem Yeats wrote in his last years, in which he summons up and joins together in one vision images from his past in Ireland. After O'Leary comes his father, remembered as he defied the crowd from the stage of the Abbey Theatre during the *Playboy* riots:

> 'My father upon the Abbey stage, before him a raging crowd:
> "This land of Saints"; and then as the applause died out,
> "Of plaster Saints"; his beautiful mischievous head thrown back.'

Standish O'Grady is recalled in a moment of drunken eloquence; Augusta Gregory at her great ormolu table before a lighted window, refusing to let any threat of violence intimidate her; Maud Gonne in a moment's repose:

> 'Maud Gonne at Howth Station waiting a train,
> Pallas Athene in that straight back and arrogant head:
> All the Olympians: a thing never known again.'

O'Leary's noble head is perhaps more vividly shown in T. W. Rolleston's photographs of 1894 (91, 92) than in the oil by John Butler Yeats (93), or in the bust by Sheppard in the Municipal Gallery, Dublin, (94) although one might have thought bronze particularly appropriate for the stern Roman quality that Yeats admired in him. Lady Gregory wrote of O'Leary: 'The grand lines of the massive head, the eyes full of smouldering fire, might be those of some ancient prophet understanding his people's doom'. This is certainly in the face. And Lady Gregory is saying what Yeats, too, thought about O'Leary. To O'Leary Yeats owed his introduction to the traditions of nationalism; and found in him the living embodiment of true nationalism: heroic, suffering, uncompromising. It is O'Leary whom he sets against the present leaders of the nationalist movement in *September 1913*.

'Romantic Ireland's dead and gone,
It's with O'Leary in the grave.'

Yeats speaks of O'Leary's 'moral genius', and would quote repeatedly his apophthegm 'there are things that a man must not do to save a nation'. Lonely, aristocratic, aloof but passionate, he would not allow any pleas of the needs of a nation to blur the outlines of good and bad, in action or in literature. Yeats saw him as a Cato or a Brutus; Lady Gregory as the prophet who rebukes as well as leads his chosen people.

Of Yeats's father, John Butler Yeats, there is room to say little, or of that sharp and persistent dialogue he and his son maintained: an essential element in the poet's formation. He figures little in his son's verse, but here a single gesture is caught and recorded, mischievous, irreverent, and totally unexpected. The mischief is in the self-portrait from the National Portrait Gallery in London (95) though not in Tuohy's portrait in Dublin (96) and all these notes were in his life: as unpredictable as his painting.

Yeats wrote that O'Leary 'alone had personality, a point of view not made for the crowd's sake, but for self-expression'. O'Leary's head, his father's head and words, O'Grady's glowing nonsense, Lady Gregory's defiance, a glimpse of Maud Gonne's physical splendour, all these things are 'moments' or 'gestures', 'moments' which declare the 'personality', the intrinsic being, free, aristocratic.

VII LISSADELL

'Your sister and yourself,' Yeats wrote to Eva Gore-Booth in 1916, 'two beautiful figures among the great trees of Lissadell, are among the dear memories of my youth'. Built in 1832, a plain late Georgian house of dark grey granite, Lissadell stands among the woods that go down to the sands of Lissadell bay (97). It lies ten miles from Sligo and five from Drumcliff. The windows of the south front look out over the bay, past Rosses Point to the hill of Knocknarea crowned with the tomb of Queen Maeve. Lissadell was the home of the Gore-Booths, an enlightened family of the Protestant ascendancy. On his first visit in 1894, Yeats found the two daughters of the house, Constance (1868-1927) and Eva (1870-1926), eager listeners to his talk about the Irish literary revival. When they were both dead, moved by what they had been when he first knew them and by what they had become, he wrote at Seville in October and November of 1927 his delicate, yet intense elegy, *In Memory of Eva Gore-Booth and Constance Markiewicz.*

Here he blends tender recollections and fantasy with a deeply serious judgement not only upon them but upon himself. Those girls when he first met them, so eager and so beautiful, and yet so different in their types of beauty, within the great classical house, must have seemed embodiments of the order to which they belonged – the aristocratic tradition expressed equally in architecture as in life. Historically, Yeats had glimpsed the last flowering moment of the Protestant ascendancy, as in this poem he realises. Something of such quality emerges in the photographs we show first, taken from one of the Gore-Booth family albums for the years 1886 to 1888, when Constance, the elder, was barely twenty. Eva's and Constance's life ranged between Lissadell, Dublin, London and the country houses of their parents' friends. Their futures seemed formally pre-determined: coming out, presentation at court, the suitable marriage. The serenity and opulence of the great house appears in the family photographs, whether they show Constance in her enormous hat (98), taking part in family theatricals (99), in her first ball dress (100), or among the Pre-Raphaelite and Japanese disarray of the room the sisters shared for their painting and drawing, and reading (101). Yet with all its graceful leisure, such a life could not contain them. The eagerness with which the two girls listened to Yeats in the bay-windowed room – great windows open to the South – full of the apparatus of their leisure, must have been an index of their restlessness. Constance, though a famous and reckless horsewoman – Eva too rode fearlessly, but Constance was said to be the finest horsewoman in Ireland – painted, and even those early photographs of her seem to show an element of wilfullness. She always, through gesture or expression, quite deliberately isolates herself from the carefully posed and smiling group (102). Eva was already writing verse. Remote and timid – the gazelle of the poem – she is also nearly always shown as looking down or away (103).

To these girls, Yeats came as a reminder of the world outside, of freedom: he brought dreams of an Ireland renewed culturally through 'mysticism' and literature. And for Yeats too this visit was important: the young middle-class poet, through his growing reputation, had been invited into an aristocratic house.

At the turn of the century, both girls left home. Eva went to do social work in Manchester, and became more and more deeply associated with the organisation of women workers in textile factories, struggling to organise them into trade unions and to fix conditions and hours for them, running papers, interviewing members of Parliament, and taxing the frailty of her health. The work she and her friend Esther Roper did here was of enormous importance to the women's suffrage movement as it developed towards its militant phase. Action was accompanied, however, in her case, by an intense cultivation of the inner life – expressing itself in the study of Neo-Platonism and Indian mysticism – and of poetry.

Yet her attitude to mysticism, unlike the attitude of Yeats himself, was rather didactic. In an unpublished letter of 6th December 1898, Yeats strikingly isolates this same tendency in her poetry. 'Your gift is for putting over-serious delicate emotion into fragile rhythms – avoid every touch of rhetoric and every tendency to teach – keep before you the idea of doing a little delicate book of lyrics that nobody will know whether to call (it) romantic or religious – it would gradually help with writing with your own feeling for Irish scenery and Irish needs to give you a new and rich kind of symbol and metaphor'. The gazelle quality in Eva was a quality of sensibility no less than of physical appearance and in an unpublished section of his *Autobiography*, Yeats speaks of Mrs Shakespear as having 'the same sensitive look of destruction I had admired in Eva Gore-Booth'; the shadow of those abstractions which were to destroy her beauty no less than her poetry (104, 105).

The life of Constance now belongs to the history and legend of Ireland. She left Lissadell for Paris in 1898, where she studied painting and met and married another painter, Count Casimir de Markiewicz, an honest adventurer of great talent, and greater charm. Returning to Dublin, where she and her husband settled, their social life – and it was varied and entertaining – failed to give her what she needed. She turned to revolutionary politics and founded the Fianna Scouts who played a useful role when the moment for action came (106). In 1914, she became a member of the Citizen's Army, another revolutionary organisation, and we show a picture of her in uniform (107). There is something at once absurd and touching about this picture. The face is fragile, the cheeks sunken, the bravura of youth has vanished and has been replaced by what seems an almost factitious bravura of uniform and intended action. The violence implicit in the gun seems to be contradicted by the sad and almost resigned expression of the face. She was to become one of the leaders of the Easter 1916 insurrection, being in charge of the contingent which held Stephens Green; and after the surrender was condemned to death, but subsequently reprieved on account of her sex. When her term of imprisonment was over she returned to Ireland. In the complicated history of the next few years, she continued to play a prominent role, always as extremist (108). It was only in the last year or two of her life that the rage for action deserted her. It was at this time that Eva died. The two sisters had always been emotionally close, though absent from one another for long periods, and when Eva was gone, Constance's nature seemed to change. For the first time she discovered the resources of the inner life. There is a sad story of her in these last years speaking to a small audience with a sling round the arm she had broken cranking her old car. At this time she was living in the slums of Dublin, working for the humblest poor, not as a great lady or as politician, but as one who had identified herself with them completely and in a spirit of simple humility. She had long since rejected the manners of her caste, even the care of her physical appearance. In her statue on Stephens Green, she has been translated into myth; the apotheosis that Yeats in *Easter 1916* rather ambiguously grants her fellow-leaders of the rebellion. Yet here the image is blandly trivialized (109).

For Yeats, these lives were tragic. Eva and Constance, like Maud Gonne, had sought the abstract at the cost of life. In the process, their beauty, which was their being (110), had been murdered and with that destruction had gone the destruction of the Great House. The 'gazebo' of Yeats's poem associates several meanings (in normal Irish usage the word is not applied strictly to the 'look out' but generally to the architectural 'folly' – something to look at rather than look from): aristocratic folly, which is finally identified with a look-out tower into an Utopian future, a future that has no place for aristocratic values; and both in turn are associated with the folly of art; art that abolishes time and establishes memory.

VIII SLIGO

Yeats died in the South of France in January 1939 at the age of seventy-three and was buried at Roquebrune. It was not until 1948 that his body could be brought back to Ireland and buried, as he had wished, in Drumcliff churchyard. Drumcliff church is an unpretentious building of the early nineteenth century (113, 114, 115). It stands hidden among trees on the flat land that divides the head of Lissadell bay from the lower slopes of Ben Bulben. (111, 112). An ancestor of his father's had been rector there in the first part of the nineteenth century and the tall gaunt rectory still stands. There is an ancient Celtic Cross and the ruins of a round tower nearby. Drumcliff itself is no more than a scatter of houses and the dispersed Protestant population must have come from long distances. Sligo was the town of his mother's family, of the Middletons and Pollexfens, whose memorials are in the churchyard of St. John's. This last return to Sligo, which Yeats had planned, was a deliberate return to his beginnings. Sligo, a hard grey town with a silted harbour, the haunted hill of Knocknarea and the long limestone mass of Ben Bulben, the strands of Sligo Bay, Lough Gill with its islands, all this is the visionary landscape of Yeats's youth and of his early poems. To return to Drumcliff was to assert his identity with an ideal past, stretching from the figures of heroic legend through his own ancestors, for he saw these ancestors – 'blood that has not passed through any huckster's loin' – as part of an ideal order, whose generous virtues he opposes to the confusions of contemporary history. With this order he identifies himself in his role as poet, and so writes his epitaph with its pride of rhetoric:

'Under bare Ben Bulben's head
In Drumcliff churchyard Yeats is laid.
An ancestor was rector there
Long years ago, a church stands near,
By the road an ancient cross.
No marble, no conventional phrase;
On limestone quarried near the spot
By his command these words are cut:
     Cast a cold eye
     On life, on death
     Horseman, pass by!'

This is the last mask he assumed (116).

D. J. Gordon/Ian Fletcher

I THE TOWER

53 *Thoor Ballylee by Robert Gregory; sepia drawing in the collection of Mrs W. B. Yeats.*

54 Thoor Ballylee.

55 Thoor Ballylee; view from ground-floor window to stream and bridge.

56 Thoor Ballylee; view from the roof to ruined cottage and walled garden.

57 ⎫ Thoor Ballylee; views of river and landscape from the roof.
58 ⎬ Photographs 54 to 59 by Studio Yann, Galway, 1957.
59 ⎭

II COOLE PARK AND LADY GREGORY

60 Coole Park, avenue of ilex. Photograph by Studio Yann, Galway, 1957.

61 Coole Park, front. Photograph from Vere R. T. Gregory, *The House of Gregory,* Dublin, 1943; original by E. J. Treston, Gort.

62 Coole Park, front, a pastel by W. B. Yeats, present whereabouts unknown; from a print in the collection of Mrs W. B. Yeats. Photograph by College Studios, Dublin.

63 Coole Park; view from the site of the front door.

64 Coole Park; view towards the woods, the path to the lake.

65 Coole Park; path to the gardens.

66 Coole Park; the formal gardens. Photographs 63–66 by Studio Yann, Galway, 1957.

67 Coole Park, library, by W. B. Yeats; pastel drawing in the collection of Mrs W. B. Yeats. Photograph by College Studios, Dublin.

D

68 **Lady Gregory in a room at Coole by J. B. Yeats, between 1896 and 1908; oil painting in the collection of Mrs D.P. O'Brian, Gort. Photograph by Studio Yann, Galway.**

69 **Lady Gregory by A. Mancini, 1906; oil painting in the Municipal Gallery, Dublin. Photograph by Sparkes, Dublin.**

70 **Lady Gregory by J. B. Yeats, 1905; drawing in the collection of the Abbey Theatre, Dublin. Photograph by Pembroke Studios, Dublin.**

71 Lady Gregory by Flora Lion, 1911; lithograph, in the National Portrait Gallery, London.

72 Lady Gregory, photograph by Ruth Shine, Lindsey House, Chelsea, June 1911. Print from Miss Elizabeth Coxhead.

73 and 74 **Lady Gregory by Sir Jacob Epstein, 1910; bronze bust in the Municipal Gallery, Dublin. Photographs by Sparkes, Dublin.**

III ROBERT GREGORY

75 Robert Gregory from a Phoenix Cricket Club group photograph, c1908. Photograph by

76 **Robert Gregory by C. H. Shannon, 1906; oil painting in the Municipal Gallery, Dublin. Photograph by Sparkes, Dublin. (Pl. 7)**

IV LIONEL JOHNSON

77 Lionel Johnson as a schoolboy, 1885. Photographer unknown.

78 Lionel Johnson in a school group, Winchester College, 1883. Photograph by

79 Lionel Johnson, detail from No. 78. (Pl. 8)

J. M. SYNGE

80 **J. M. Synge by J. B. Yeats; oil painting in the Municipal Gallery, Dublin.**

81 *J. M. Synge by J. B. Yeats, 1905; pencil drawing in the collection of Professor D. J. Gordon.*

82 **J. M. Synge by Robert Gregory, 1904; chalk drawing in the National Gallery of Ireland, Dublin.**

GEORGE POLLEXFEN

83 George Pollexfen by J. B. Yeats; pencil drawing in the collection of Mrs W. B. Yeats.

84 George Pollexfen from a photograph in the collection of Mrs W. B. Yeats. (Pl. 9).

V MAUD GONNE

85 Maud Gonne at the age of twenty-one (1887); a Studio portrait by F. Czira; Mrs C. MacBride's collection.

86 Maud Gonne, about the same time; a studio portrait, photographer unknown; Mrs C. MacBride's collection.

87 Maud Gonne, about the same time; a studio portrait, photographer unknown; Mrs C. MacBride's collection.

88 Maud Gonne by Sarah Purser; oil painting in the Municipal Gallery, Dublin.

89 **Maud Gonne by Lawrence Campbell, 1932; portrait bust, plaster bronzed, in the Municipal Gallery, Dublin. Photograph by Sparkes, Dublin.**

90 Maud Gonne in her eighties. Photograph by Horvath; Irish Tourist Board.

VI JOHN O'LEARY

91 and 92 John O'Leary. Photographs by T. W. Rolleston, 1894; Lady Albery's collection.

93 **John O'Leary by J. B. Yeats, 1904; oil painting in the National Gallery of Ireland, Dublin.**

94 John O'Leary by Oliver Sheppard; bronze bust in the Municipal Gallery, Dublin.

JOHN BUTLER YEATS

95 **Self portrait by John Butler Yeats; pencil drawing in the National Portrait Gallery, London.** (Pl. 10).

96 John Butler Yeats by Patrick Tuohy; oil painting in the National Gallery of Ireland, Dublin. Photograph by Mason.

VII LISSADELL

97 Lissadell. Photographer unknown; Lady Gore-Booth's collection.

98 Constance Gore-Booth. Photograph from Gore-Booth family album, c1886.

99 Constance Gore-Booth at Lissadell. Photograph frpm Gore-Booth family album, c1886.

100 Constance Gore-Booth in her first ball-dress. Photograph from Gore-Booth family album, c1886. (Pl. 12).

101 Constance Gore-Booth in her work room. Photograph from Gore-Booth family album, c1886.

102 House-party group at Lissadell. Photograph from Gore-Booth family album, c1886.

103 Eva Gore-Booth. Photograph from Gore-Booth family album, c1886.

104 Eva Gore-Booth. Photograph from Gore-Booth family album, c1886. (Pl. 11).

105 Eva Gore-Booth. Photograph from Gore-Booth family album, c1886.

106 Constance Markiewicz in her uniform as leader of the Fianna Scouts. Photograph by Keogh, Dublin, c1912.

107 Constance Markiewicz in the uniform of the Citizen Army. Photograph by Keogh, Dublin, c1914.

108 Constance Markiewicz as public speaker. Photograph by Keogh, Dublin.

108a Constance Markiewicz in later life. Photograph by Keogh, Dublin. (Pl. 13).

109 Constance Markiewicz, monument on Stephens Green, Dublin by Seamus Murphy, 1956. Photograph by James Mulkerns, Dublin, 1957.

110 Eva Gore-Booth, the later years, c1924. Photographer unknown. Reproduced in *Poems* by Eva Gore-Booth, 1929.

VIII SLIGO

111 Ben Bulben.

112 Ben Bulben from the South West.

113 Ben Bulben and Drumcliff Church.

114 The Celtic Cross and Drumcliff Church.

115 Drumcliff Churchyard.

116 Yeats's headstone, Drumcliff churchyard. Photographs 111–116 by A. A. Toher, Esq, Sligo.

76 *Robert Gregory*
    by C. H. Shannon, 1906
    Courtesy of the Municipal Gallery, Dublin

Plate 7

79　Lionel Johnson, 1885

Plate 8

Plate 9

95 *Self-Portrait*
by J. B. Yeats
Courtesy of the National Portrait Gallery

Plate 10

Plate 11

Plate 12

108a Constance Markiewicz (née Gore-Booth) in later life

Plate 13

THE POET AND THE THEATRE

'Theatre business, management of men'

'Players and painted stage took all my love'

I   W. B. Yeats's interest in the theatre originated far earlier than is commonly supposed. His father had believed that the greatest poetry was essentially dramatic, since it could represent most fully the single defining gesture that isolates the highest human quality – 'personality'. And it was under his father's influence that W. B. Yeats began his career in the middle 1880s with several brief poetic plays, derivative and unactable. In March 1888, J. B. Yeats took his family for the second time to the small artistic suburb of Bedford Park. This consciously 'aesthetic' community of artists, poets, scholars and actors lived in Queen Anne style red-brick houses grouped round a club-house which was intended as a focus for their diverse energies. The exterior of the club-house is unremarkable, 'so plain and simple it might easily be taken for a gentleman's residence' (117), but the interior, altered in the Edwardian period, amounted almost to a parody of art-for-art's sake eclecticism. *The Building News* for 3rd January 1880 has the fullest description:

> 'The walls are hung with Japanese paper of dark tone, and with choice specimens of old tapestry. . . . In the assembly room is a mantel-piece exhibited by (Aldam) Heaton in the last Paris Exhibition, the work is painted with clear green colours and relieved by gesso-work in transparent colours and large gilded human figures . . . in the rear of the room a stage is being fitted up.'

It was on this stage on 5th May 1890 that John Todhunter's play *A Sicilian Idyll* was first performed. Yeats had encouraged Todhunter (118), a close friend of J. B. Yeats, and later to become a member of the Irish Literary Society and of the Rhymers' Club, to write his pastoral; and in the account of the *Idyll* Yeats wrote for an American paper in June 1890, (reprinted in *Letters to the New Island*, 1934) he refers to Todhunter's version of Euripides' *Helena in Troas*, which the total artist E. W. Godwin had produced, with a strictly classical set that took archaeological realism to its extreme, at Hengler's Circus in June 1886 (119).

> '*Helena in Troas* a few years since, was the talk of a London season. Its sonorous verse, united to the rhythmical motions of the white-robed chorus, and the solemnity of burning incense, produced a semi-religious effect new to the modern stage.
> . . . Once get your audience in that mood and you can do anything with it.'

Yeats was in Ireland at the time *Helena in Troas* was staged, but in a review of Todhunter's *The Poison Flower* in 1891, he is again concerned with the conquest of a popular audience by the poetic play.

> '*Helena in Troas*, acted four or five years ago, was an immense success. It not merely drew the cultivated public who cared for poetry or for Greek drama, but filled the theatre with the ordinary run of theatre-goers.'

And in his notice of *A Sicilian Idyll* Yeats had observed that 'the long room with its black panels and gilt Cupids had been crowded with really distinguished audiences'.

Yeats can hardly have failed to remark that the actors, stage-designer, composer of incidental music, designer of costumes and stage properties of the *Idyll*, and the author himself, all lived in Bedford Park. Indeed the designer, H. M. Paget, played the major male role and devised the poster advertising the play – the design was to be repeated on the programme of the later production at St. George's Hall (120). The *Sicilian Idyll* (121, 122) witnessed the appearance of Florence Farr (123, 124), whose acting in *The Poison Flower* a year later was for Yeats 'as intense and passionate as her rendering of the role of Amaryllis in the *Idyll* was graceful and self-contained; . . . since then (she has) become well known to theatre-goers through her acting in Ibsen's *Rosmersholm*. She will always, however, be best, I believe, in poetic drama'. And in the *Auto-biographies* he was to write that her 'speech was music, the poetry acquired a nobility, a passionate austerity that made it akin to the great poetry of the world . . . the seeming natural expression of the image'.

This encouragement of Todhunter shows Yeats's tentative approach to a poetic non-naturalistic drama, which could not be staged in the contemporary commercial theatre. In Bedford Park he was encouraged to begin his search for a new drama, a new audience and a new way of acting. By April 1889 he had begun work on *The Countess Cathleen'* which was published in 1892, and *The Shadowy Waters.* Todhunter's *A Comedy of Sighs* was performed in 1894 at the Avenue Theatre as part of Florence Farr's season of plays – financed by Miss Annie Horniman – together with Shaw's *Arms and the Man,* and with Yeats's *The Land of Heart's Desire* as a curtain raiser (125). In effect, this not conspicuously successful venture involved a frontal assault on a West End audience. The programme cover and a poster were designed by Aubrey Beardsley (126) while Miss Farr herself tried to startle journalists by declaring that her season represented a new movement in the English theatre. In *The Sketch* of 28th March 1894, there is a not unamusing account of Miss Farr's conception of the Avenue season. ' "You see we are nothing if not advanced", began the future Lady Brandon, merrily. . . . "And in what sense, Miss Farr, do you understand the word 'advanced?' " "It is by no means easy to answer that question, but perhaps I can best express what I think if I say that we consider absolute realism only a phase of dramatic art, and in this play (i.e. Todhunter's *A Comedy of Sighs)* we hope to go a step further – in fact we shall try to use symbolism to express realities" '. *A Comedy of Sighs* (Dr. Todhunter's M.S. is in the Library of the University of Reading) can hardly have made Miss Farr's answer easier. It is in drawing-room prose, with some mild satiric wit, and its heroine is a new woman with not quite enough courage for her convictions. The characters resemble Henry Arthur Jones rather than Ibsen. Yeats with his usual practical sense perhaps realised by this time that neither his own nor Todhunter's play was strong enough for the honour of 'going a step further'. There is some reservation in his early praise of *Helena in Troas* and the *Sicilian Idyll,* but in the *Autobiographies* he came to agree with Wilde that their blank verse owed more to 'the courtesy of the printer than the genius of the poet'. Events were to justify his hesitations. Todhunter's new play was a failure; what success Miss Farr had was confined to Shaw's *Arms and the Man,* and no other play of Yeats's was performed publicly until 1899, when the Irish Literary Theatre staged *The Countess Cathleen* in Dublin.

II It was from the Irish Literary Theatre and its immediate successor, the Irish National Theatre Society, that the Abbey Theatre was finally born in December 1904 (127) with a building and endowment provided by Miss Horniman (127a).

Yeats was perfectly clear from the beginning about what he wanted an Irish drama and a National Theatre to do, and said so repeatedly in *Beltaine* and *Samhain*. He looked back and saw their enterprise as kin to many attempts that had been made in the last decade to break the power of the commercial theatre: to the Bedford Park experiments; to Grein's Independent Theatre; to Antoine and Lugné-Poe in Paris; to Norway; to Germany. But the Irish movement would have one unique characteristic: it was to be a National Theatre, and National in Yeats's sense – there was to be a good deal of trouble later about this sense – which meant that it was to forge the un-created conscience of the race. Its plays were to be doctrinal to a nation.

The means: poetic drama in its purest definition. His own part was to create a heroic drama appealing to his audience at the deepest level of feeling by the use of the most ancient heroic symbols. Symbol and poetry unite the audience; in this union they realise a national consciousness. The effect of this drama was to be the effect of poetry itself. New methods of verse speaking and a new kind of stage design were necessary. At this time Yeats and Florence Farr were busy with their experiments in the speaking of verse to the psaltery; but about their value even Yeats's friends showed considerable scepticism. More to the point was the passionate devotion of Frank Fay to the history and methods of verse speaking. Verse was to be spoken as verse and not disguised as prose. Movement and gesture were to express only what was in the poetry, not simulate 'natural situations'. The whole apparatus of the naturalistic theatre was to be rejected.

It seems reasonably certain that from those first days at Bedford Park, Yeats had been uneasy about naturalistic staging: it would be part of his reaction against the naturalism that he found his father and his friends practising in their painting, and against the science and positivism of the age: the general reaction, in fact, which turned him to the symbol. 'Art is art because it is not nature,' Yeats was fond of quoting, and he applies this aphorism to the stage. He certainly knew about the experiments of the *Symboliste* theatre in France which grew out of the impact of Wagner in the late eighties, and created the 'Théâtre de L'Art' in the early nineties, and were carried on by Lugné-Poë in the 'Théâtre de L'Oeuvre'; *Axel* became one of his sacred books, and he was very excited about the production which he saw in Paris in 1894. The work of Lugné-Poë was known and seen in England; and there was always Arthur Symons's gossip. The way was thus prepared for Yeats's enthusiastic recognition of Gordon Craig's first experiments in design which belong to the year 1901. In Craig's work, Yeats recognised the art of stage presentation for which he had been looking; it was, he thought, an art that belonged purely to the stage, whose aim was to let the play express itself with the maximum intensity and freedom through a bold disposition of colour, shape and movement. Yet Yeats saw one defect in Craig's work. Craig was not really interested in the actor. And for Yeats, everything finally came down to the actor speaking and moving.

Very little seems to be known in detail about the staging of the early Irish plays. Yeats certainly got rid of the conventional scene – painter whom he abhorred. And poverty reinforced the theory by making simplicity necessary. But how far he was satisfied with the results, or believed that they really announced 'the hour of convention and decoration and ceremony' we cannot say. It is not very likely that he was delighted with the costumes, designed and laboriously made by Miss Horniman for *The King's Threshold* (128, 129, 130, 131). All of these early photographs have an air of the intolerably amateur, of a crudely staged performance in a village hall; but this, we know, is not a true account. The accounts given by the critics, and their praise, are not to be questioned. We know that of all the early designers, Yeats approved most of Robert Gregory. In 1903 he designed the costumes for *The Hour Glass* (132). They were 'purple, played against a green cloth', and his mother adds 'it was our first attempt at the decorative staging long demanded by Mr Yeats'. Gregory also staged *The Shadowy Waters* in 1904 (133, 134), on 'the sloping deck of a galley, blue and dim, the sails and dresses are green, the ornaments all of copper'. Blue, purple, green, copper: the colours of Morris and after. The general effect of Gregory's staging – so far as we can judge – shown, for example, in his *Deirdre* setting of 1906 (135) is of a vaguely Celtic inspiration, a late and simplified Pre-Raphaelitism. This is confirmed by his fully executed picture of an ideal set for that play (136, 136a). As a general designer, Gregory probably belonged to that persisting Arts and Crafts tradition which in England did not become Art Nouveau. (A portrait of Arthur Sinclair (136a) in one of his mother's plays shows, however, considerable liveliness). When the play was revived for Mrs Patrick Campbell in 1908, in Dublin and London, it was Mrs Patrick Campbell who was conspicuous: but a set by Gregory was used (137, 138, 139). Collaboration with Gordon Craig never really quite happened, though he did four designs which were published in *Plays for an Irish Theatre* in 1911, and in the same year seems to have designed masks for the blind man in *On Baile's Strand,* and the fool in *The Hour Glass;* and the Abbey acquired a set of his screens. Yeats was particularly anxious to persuade those English artists whom he most admired, Sturge Moore, and Charles Ricketts, to work for him. Ricketts's stage designs were of great originality, lavish and fantastic in conception, daring and extravagant in their use of colour. Those who were to be so astonished in 1911 by what Bakst created for Diaghilev might have found something of the effect before that in Ricketts's work; and behind both are the same influences, oriental, and, probably, Gustave Moreau. Yeats, however, may have found Ricketts rather elusive; but for the Abbey's London visits in 1914 and 1915, he did design costumes for *The King's Threshold* and *On Baile's Strand* (140, 141, 142, 143).

The Abbey was brilliantly successful: it became, and rightly so, one of the famous theatres in Europe. Yet the triumph of the Abbey, by a sad paradox, Yeats thought to be his own defeat. His own heroic moralities did not achieve more than a success of esteem; and his relationship to Irish nationalism became more and more ambiguous. The programme he had proposed had little relevance to the realities of the Irish situation. Initiative in the national struggle had passed from the literary middle classes, the sympathising ascendancy, and even the parliamentary party. There was again a demand for a simpler and more pragmatic definition of patriotism than either Yeats or Lady Gregory was prepared to provide. The polemics of the Synge and Hugh Lane controversies, involving as they did competing notions of the duties of writers and the immediate needs of Ireland, deepened Yeats's sense of estrangement and for some years there is a gap in his dramatic production. His one unquestioned popular success in Ireland was still *Cathleen ni Houlihan.* The irony is palpable. When it was first produced in 1902, Maud Gonne played the old woman (144) and, whatever Yeats had intended, the response her performance evoked was direct, simple, and patriotic in a most uncomplicated way (144a).

III When he returned to the drama, Yeats had found a new model. In 1916, the Cuala Press, managed by Yeats's two sisters, published Ezra Pound's redaction of the American scholar Ernest Fenollosa's versions of some Japanese Noh plays. For some years Pound had been an intimate friend of Yeats and those translations made a decisive impression on him.

The effects in Europe from the eighteen-sixties of the discovery of

Japanese painting are well known; less well known are the earlier signs of interest in Japanese literature and drama (145, 146). In 1892, Sir Edwin Arnold wrote a poem describing a Noh dance and published a translation of a Noh play, and in Osman Edwards's *Japanese Plays and Playfellows,* which appeared in 1901, there is a chapter on religious drama, with illustrations. In 1901 Japanese actors visited London and there is, in the same period, some periodical literature on the subject, such as M. A. Hinks's 'The Art of Dancing in Japan' in *The Fortnightly Review* in 1906. Marie Stopes in her *A Journal from Japan,* 1910, described Noh and in 1912 published her *Plays of Old Japan* in collaboration with Professor J. Sakurai; and here we find the play called 'Motomezuka', which we know Yeats to have admired. Our prints showing the Noh (147, 148, 149, 150) stage, masks, and figures in action are part of a series dated about 1902. Furthermore, in a circle to which Yeats was deeply attached, there existed a most lively interest in the Noh, as we see from the descriptions in Oswald Sickert's remarkable letters written from Japan to Charles Ricketts in 1916: Ricketts, already a connoisseur of Japanese art, was at this time one of the mentors Yeats acknowledged.

It was in 1912 that Mrs Fenollosa had given her husband's papers to Pound, and in 1913 that Yeats first spent the winter in Sussex, in a cottage shared with Pound. One evening in 1915, Pound went up to a young man in the Café Royal and asked 'Are you Chinese or Japanese?' – to quote from Michio Ito's reminiscences recorded by Anthony Thwaite. The young man soon found himself involved in helping Pound to study the Noh. Somewhat to his surprise, for he had not seen a Noh play since he was seven years old, and had come to Europe to study 'free' dancing, the kind of dancing we associate with Loïe Fuller or Isadora Duncan.

However, he sent to Tokio for books on the Noh, and set himself to learn the formal language of its dance, so that he could demonstrate to Pound and his friends; and so learnt in England the value of his native tradition. In Alvin Langdon Coburn's photographs he is tremendously impressive, masked as a fox – the mask was designed and made by Dulac – or with a naked sword: an image of heroic action (151, 152, 153, 154).

Yeats found in the Noh an aristocratic drama, written by a caste of dramatists, highly privileged and requiring no compromise with any public. The Noh dramatist worked within a severe convention: elements that particularly attracted Yeats were the total absence of naturalistic representation in setting or in action: the stylization, in fact, of the whole drama in terms of mask, gesture and ritual attitude. The prints we show, illustrate the repertory of masks; the bare stage offering possibilities of conveying heroic action through remote and hieratic gesture. This is what Yeats had dreamed of and what he had attempted to achieve. Perhaps it was not only his audience he had to blame for his failure, but the formula he had adopted. Mask and dance were two of the supreme images through which he had come to express reality: Mask, paradoxically, man's best means of creating and communicating what he is, redeemed from accident; and the dance, in which as the dancer's character is lost, his 'being' is, paradoxically, intensified. There now seemed to be the possibility of combining Mask and Dance with the living image, which he had always conceived the play to be; an image which shared the properties of the images of poetry, or of the visual arts - indeed perhaps transcending these since it achieves the Union of the Arts: the symbolist dream. Wild though this may seem, Yeats was not alone in requiring such qualities of drama. In his idea that expression is only possible through the impersonal, he is very close once more to Gordon Craig, who was writing in these same years: 'the mask is the only right medium of portraying the expressions of the soul as shown through the expressions of the face', and whose aim was to create on the stage through flesh and blood, paint, light and cloth, a unified image.

It was only now, then, that the Japanese tradition, in its encounter with this poet made a creative contribution to English literature: an encounter so curiously mediated, and successful precisely because it was so mediated, as to offer something that he had already half known. The first of these plays and probably the closest to the Noh convention is *At the Hawk's Well,* produced in the drawing-room of Lady Cunard's house in Cavendish Square on Sunday afternoon, 2nd April 1916; and 'a few days later it was revived in Lady Islington's big drawing-room in Chesterfield Gardens for the benefit of a war charity. There was a platform jutting out from the wall and some three hundred fashionable people, including Queen Alexandra, were round the platform on three sides, and once more my muses were but half welcome', to follow Yeats's own account in *Instead of a Theatre* which he printed in Holbrook Jackson's *To-day,* May 1917; but the audience at Lady Cunard's had gleamed with fashion, politics and literature; and Pound had brought Mr T. S. Eliot – 'unmatched corduroys flanked by bowler and tightly rolled umbrella'. Costumes and masks were made by Edmund Dulac, the musicians were Dulac, Mrs Mann, and Mr Foulds; the Young Man – Cuchulain

– was Henry Ainley; the Old Man, Allan Wade (155, 156). The Guardian of the Well was Ito himself, who danced the Hawk Dance (157, 158, 159). Visitors to the London Zoo recently had been rather surprised to see him imitating the movement of hawks outside their cage, watched by a fascinated Yeats. Alvin Langdon Coburn, the only photographer Yeats trusted, photographed the actors.

Mr Eliot said that hearing *At the Hawk's Well* altered his whole view of Yeats. He now realised that Yeats was not simply a rather faded poet of the nineties. The editor of *To-day,* writing on Yeats in that same issue, commented 'at the age of fifty-one, with something that seems like disappointment, he would seem to be abandoning a folk movement for an aristocratic', and goes on:

> 'It is one of the ironies of propaganda that Yeats himself, inspirer of the Irish Literary movement and founder of the Irish drama, should in his own work have hit widest of the mark at which he aimed . . . to the folk, to those whose interest in art is far behind their interest in life, he had given almost nothing.'

Records of later performances of the dance plays in Yeats's own life time are disappointingly meagre. But to show the use of masks there are two fine photographs of the Fool and Blind Man from Terence Gray's Cambridge Festival Theatre production of *Baile's Strand,* January - February 1927 (160, 161). And there is the unexpected story of *The Only Jealousy of Emer.*

Albert van Dalsum, now Holland's leading actor, then a young man just beginning his career, deeply interested in the non-naturalistic drama, and under the immediate influence of the German expressionist theatre, read *The Only Jealousy of Emer* when it was first published in *Four Plays for Dancers* (1921). In 1922, he organised a performance in Amsterdam. He saw this as, before anything else, an experiment in the use of the mask (he was familiar with Gordon Craig's writings) and the style of acting that this imposed, the slow, grave, extended gestures and movements; he saw the adoption of the mask as an attempt to rediscover style, and as an 'act of self-liberation', relevant in an age which realised the profound power of the irrational, the mystery behind the mask. He was helped by the dancer Lili Green. For the masks he turned to the sculptor Hildo Krop, whose art, developed from close connexions with the Arts and Crafts movement, touched life at many points. These masks were of papier maché, with woollen hair, painted basically in ivory, with deep shadows. Mr Krop has made for us a replica of the Cuchulain mask (162). The costumes are severely stylised in deep pure colours (163,

164, 165, 166) with very simple geometrical patterns, in sharp contrast. Our photograph of the unfolding of the cloth which opens the play conveys something of the severe and distanced drama which Yeats intended. Later Mr Krop made from the plaster models the five bronzes which we show (167, 168, 169, 170, 171): and the dark metal confers on the bold definitions that sombre human, non-human austerity which the stage mask isolated from the life of the performance can hardly show. Mr van Dalsum revived *The Only Jealousy* for a single performance in Amsterdam in 1926, when our photographs were taken. After this, a Dutch friend of Yeats's showed him photographs of the bronzes that had appeared a year before in an *avant-garde* Dutch periodical (172, 173). Yeats was immensely impressed. He had the photographs of the production sent to him, and rewrote the play as *Fighting the Waves* – produced at the Abbey in 1929 (and repeated at the Lyric, Hammersmith) with Krop's masks, choreography by Ninette de Valois, and costumes by Miss Travers Smith (174, 175).

D. J. Gordon / Ian Fletcher

117 Bedford Park Club-house.

118 John Todhunter, January 1899. Photograph by Elliot & Fry.

119 *"Helena in Troas" by J. Todhunter; water colour by H. M. Paget, 1886, in the collection of the University of Reading.*

120 *"A Sicilian Idyll", poster announcement; water-colour by H. M. Paget, 1890, in the collection of the University of Reading.*

121 Sketches of the performance of *A Sicilian Idyll*, St. George's Hall, 3rd July 1890. *The Daily Graphic.*

122 *A Sicilian Idyll*, characters in costume. Photographer unknown, 1890; Victoria and Albert Museum, Enthoven Collection.

123 Florence Farr in the costume she wore as Amaryllis in *A Sicilian Idyll.* Photographer unknown, 1890.

124 Florence Farr in the costume she wore as Amaryllis in *A Sicilian Idyll;* a second photograph. Photographer unknown, 1890.

125 *The Land of Heart's Desire.* Photographs from *The Sketch,* 25th April 1894; print from Victoria and Albert Museum, Enthoven Collection.

126 *Poster for "A Comedy of Sighs" by Aubrey Beardsley, 1894; in the collection of the University of Reading.*

127 The Abbey Theatre, facade. Photograph by The Pembroke Studios, Dublin.

127a **Miss Annie Horniman by J. B. Yeats, 1904; oil painting in the collection of the Abbey Theatre, Dublin.**

128 ⎤ *The King's Threshold,* Molesworth Hall, Dublin, 1903. Photo-
129 ⎟ graphs by Chancellor, from original prints in the possession
130 ⎟ of Mrs W. B. Yeats. (Pl. 14). No. 131, stage photograph in Mrs.
131 ⎦ W. B. Yeats's collection.

132 Robert Gregory, water colour sketch for *The Hour Glass,* 1903, in the collection of Mrs W. B. Yeats.

133 ⎤ *The Shadowy Waters,* Molesworth Hall, Dublin, 1904. Sets and
and ⎬ costumes by Robert Gregory. Photographer unknown, from
134 ⎦ prints in the possession of Mrs W. B. Yeats.

135 *Deirdre,* by W. B. Yeats, Abbey Theatre, 1906. Sets by Robert Gregory. Photographer unknown, from print in the possession of Mrs W. B. Yeats.

136 *Ideal set for 'Deirdre' by Robert Gregory; oil painting in the collection of Mrs W. B. Yeats.*

136a **Arthur Sinclair (in** *'Kincora'***) by Robert Gregory; oil painting in the collection of the Abbey Theatre, Dublin. Photograph by Pembroke Studios.**

137 Mrs Patrick Campbell in W. B. Yeats's *Deirdre,* New Theatre, London, December 1908. Photographed by Chancellor, print from Victoria and Albert Museum, Enthoven Collection.

138 Naoise entrapped, W. B. Yeats's *Deirdre,* New Theatre, London, 1908. Photograph by Ellis and Walery, from *The Sketch,* 9th December 1908.

139 Last scene and death of *Deirdre,* Mrs Patrick Campbell, New Theatre, London, December 1903. Photographs by Ellis and Walery, from *The Tatler,* 9th December 1908; prints from Victoria and Albert Museum, Enthoven Collection.

140 **King Guaire in** *The King's Threshold,* **1914; wash drawing by Charles Ricketts in the collection of Mrs W. B. Yeats. Photograph, College Studios, Dublin.**

141 **Group of Kings in** *Baile's Strand,* **1915; wash drawing by Charles Ricketts in the collection of Mrs W. B. Yeats. Photograph, College Studios, Dublin.**

142 **Cuchulain in** *Baile's Strand;* **wash drawing by Charles Ricketts, 1914/1915, in the collection of Mrs W. B. Yeats. Photograph, College Studios, Dublin.**

143 **The Blind Man and Fool in** *Baile's Strand,* **1915; wash drawing by Charles Ricketts in the collection of Mrs W. B. Yeats. Photograph, College Studios, Dublin.**

144 Maud Gonne as Cathleen in *Cathleen ni Houlihan,* 1902, St. Teresa's Hall, Dublin. Stage photograph in Mrs W. B. Yeats's collection.

144a **W. B. Yeats, a Caricature by Edmund Dulac 1915; pastel drawing in the collection of the Abbey Theatre Dublin. Photograph by Pembroke Studios.**

145 *Scene from a Noh play; Japanese colour print by Kuniyoshi, 1849/53, in the Whitworth Art Gallery.*

146 *Noh Mask from the collection of the Horniman Museum and Library, London.*

147⌉
148⌊ *Prints of the Japanese Noh, c1902. University of Reading*
149 ⌈ *Collection.*
150⌋

151 Ito with a fox-mask. Photograph by Alvin Langdon Coburn, c1916. (Pl. 15).

152 Ito with a sword. Photograph by Alvin Langdon Coburn, c1916. (Pl. 16).

153 Ito in kimono and female make-up, beside a primitive mask. Photograph by Alvin Langdon Coburn, c1916.

154 Ito in ceremonial costume. Photograph by Alvin Langdon Coburn, c1916.

155 Henry Ainley, as the young Cuchulain in *At the Hawk's Well,* 1916. Photograph by Alvin Langdon Coburn. (Pl. 17).

156 Allan Wade as the Old Man in *At the Hawk's Well,* 1916. Photograph by Alvin Langdon Coburn. (Pl. 18).

157⎫
158⎬ Ito as the Guardian of the Well in *At the Hawk's Well,* 1916.
159⎭ Photographs by Alvin Langdon Coburn. (Pl. 19 and 20).

160 and 161 Blind Man and Fool in *Baile's Strand,* Festival Theatre, Cambridge, 1927. Photographer unknown, prints from originals in possession of Mrs W. B. Yeats. (Pl. 22).

162 **Mask for Cuchulain in** *The Only Jealousy of Emer;* **replica made by Mr Hildo Krop of his 1922 Mask.** (Pl. 21).

163⎫ Scenes from *The Only Jealousy of Emer,* produced by Albert
164⎩ van Dalsum, Amsterdam, 1922, 1926. Photographs by N. V.
165⎰ Vereenigde Fotobureaux, Amsterdam, from the set. Mrs W. B.
166⎭ Yeats's collection. (Pl. 23 and 24).

167⎫
168⎪
169⎬ **The masks for** *The Only Jealousy of Emer;* **bronzes by Hildo**
170⎪ **Krop in the City Museum, Amsterdam.**
171⎭

172⎰ Hildo Krop. Masks for *The Only Jealousy of Emer,* from
173⎱ *Wendingen,* 1925.

174⎰ Scenes from *Fighting the Waves,* Abbey Theatre, Dublin, 1929,
175⎱ *The Sketch,* 21st August 1929. (Pl. 25).

Plate 14

151   Ito in his fox mask, London, c.1916

Plate 15

Plate 16

155 Henry Ainley as the young Cuchulain, *At the Hawk's Well,*
London, 1916.

Plate 17

156 Allan Wade as the Old Man, *At the Hawk's Well,* London, 1916.

Plate 18

157   Ito as Guardian of the Well, *At the Hawk's Well,* London, 1916.

Plate 19

159   Ito as Guardian of the Well, *At the Hawk's Well,* London, 1916.

Plate 20

162 Mask by Hildo Krop for Cuchulain, *The Only Jealousy of Emer,*
Amsterdam, 1922.

Plate 21

161   Blind Man and Fool, *On Baile's Strand,* Festival Theatre,
Cambridge, 1926–7

Plate 22

166   *The Only Jealousy of Emer,* Amsterdam, 1926

Plate 23

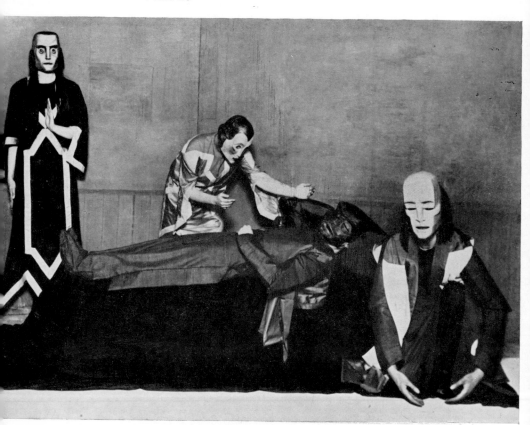

Plate 24

175 *Fighting the Waves*
     Abbey Theatre, Dublin, 1929

Plate 25

BYZANTIUM

'And therefore I have sailed the seas and come
To the holy city of Byzantium.'

I   As an historical act the composition of the Byzantium poems is a great leap, a sudden capture: an act possible only to an artist whose imagination works in the dimension of history and with its monuments and records, and strictly comparable to the appropriation of the Japanese Noh. The conditions had to be observed: the historians or grammarians had to prepare the material: it had to be fairly easily accessible to anyone who wanted to find it; and it had to give the poet the answers he, at that moment, wanted. Given the conditions, and an imagination of this sort, the result was an expropriation of a whole culture, its translation into images, intensely personal, synthetic; yet grounded on impersonal observation; and in one of their aspects acts of historical judgement; and capable of transmitting and sealing a historical view; and so becoming part of the story. We show something of Yeats's approach to Byzantium; and of selected images from the two poems, to illustrate how many of his themes and preoccupations they hold.

The jump is – and to present it in this way is hardly to oversimplify – to 'And therefore I have sailed the seas and come to the holy city of Byzantium' from Voltaire's declaration that Byzantine history was 'a worthless repository of declamation, and miracles disgraceful to the human mind'. Or from Gibbon's assurance, when he reduces Santa Sophia:

> 'A magnificent temple is a laudable monument of national taste and religion, and the enthusiast who entered the dome of St. Sophia might be tempted to suppose that it was the residence, or even the workmanship, of the Deity. Yet how dull is the artifice, how insignificant the labour, if it be compared with the formation of the vilest insect that crawls upon the surface of the temple.'

Or dismisses the throne of Solomon:

> '(The Emperor's) fanciful magnificence employed the skill and patience of such artists as the times could afford: but the taste of Athens would have despised their frivolous and costly labours; a golden tree, with its leaves and branches, which sheltered a multitude of birds, warbling their artificial notes and two lions of massy gold, and of the natural size, who looked and roared like their brethren of the forest. . . .'

Or confidently rejects a thousand years:

> 'In the revolution of ten centuries, not a single discovery was made to exalt the dignity or promote the happiness of mankind. . . .'

A judgement to be echoed, with less justification because on far less secure premises, by the nineteenth-century rationalist historians, so that even a Lecky could write:

> 'of that Byzantine Empire, the universal verdict of history is that it constitutes with scarcely an exception, the most thoroughly vicious form that civilization has assumed.'

II   Yeats's first direct contact with Byzantine art was at Ravenna in 1907, when he made a tour of Northern Italy with Lady Gregory and her son. This visit would not appear to have left a decisive impression on his work: his interest was concentrated on Italian painting, particularly that of the Renaissance; and the cultivated tourist was still likely to visit Ravenna for Dante's sake. His main guide book was Reinach's *Apollo* (1907) which has little on the subject of Byzantine art. It was rather the historical studies he engaged in after 1918 that turned his attention to the subject.

What particularly fascinated him now was the search for cyclic patterns in history. He was reading such books as Burkitt's *Early Eastern Christianity* (1904), W. G. Holmes's elementary *The Age of Justinian and Theodora* (1905/1907) with its description of the Golden Throne of the Emperors; Mrs Arthur Strong's *Apotheosis and the After Life* (1915), and Strzygowski's *Origin of Christian Church Art* (1923) – 'searching out signs of the whirling gyres of the historical cone as we see it and hoping that by this study I may see deeper into what is to come'. This search issued in *A Vision* (1925), that strange construct, which has troubled his admirers so much, an amalgam of history, psychology and eschatology, in which Byzantium as historical, no less than as an artistic entity, has an important role.

Such new found interest in the historical Byzantium made Yeats wish to visit the more easily accessible monuments of its art. And so he and Mrs Yeats planned – in company with Mr and Mrs Ezra Pound – a visit to Sicily to see the great mosaics at Palermo and Cefalu. It would appear that the visit took place in January 1925. During this time Yeats was still working on *A Vision,* and the section *Dove and Swan* in which his famous account of Byzantium appeared, concludes with a note: 'finished at Syracuse in 1925'. (The dating may be romantic, but in any case shows what Yeats considered the appropriate site for this composition). From Sicily, Mr and Mrs Yeats went for a short time to Capri and then on to Rome by the end of February 1925. In Rome, they concentrated on seeing the finest examples of Early Christian art. The whole tour lasted for about six weeks. Yeats brought back with him photographs of those monuments which had most interested him. Particularly notable is the mosaic at La Zisa, Palermo, with its two palm-trees between peacocks, flanking formalized fruit-bearing trees with birds in the branches, emblems of immortality (176). On the apse at San Clemente in Rome the Redeemer is shown on a cross with its base in foliage and birds perching on its arms (177, 178). In an article on *The Sacred Dance* by G. R. S. Mead (*The Quest,* 1910) which Yeats knew, S. Clemente is singled out as possessing a choir raised to form a ceremonial dancing-floor; Mead was arguing that there had been liturgical provision for a dance symbolising the dance of the blessed in Paradise. The mosaics on the tribune of San Prassede provide striking counterparts of the sages in their golden fire (179, 180, 181).

Before the visit to Ravenna in 1907, Yeats must have been aware of the idea of Byzantium as it recurred in books and discussions. The late nineteenth century had inherited an image of Byzantium as the history of decadence – a culture frozen at a late stage in its development. But a new school of Byzantine scholars became active in France in the 1880s–the fathers, in fact, of our present notion of Byzantium. The great English representatives of this new scholarship were J. B. Bury, whose *History of the Later Roman Empire* appeared in 1889, and O. M. Dalton, whose *Byzantine Art* was published in 1911 – Yeats bought a copy of this some years later. Texier and Pullan's study of Byzantine church architecture in Asia Minor dates from 1864; and in 1894 the first serious study of Santa Sophia, by Lethaby and Swainson, appeared; and the eighteen-nineties saw the beginnings of Westminster Cathedral. But through the nineteenth century in England serious interest in Byzantine art was to be found in such an obvious book as Lindsay's *History of*

Christian Art; and Ruskin's studies of St. Mark's opened a new field to many. Such activity in the world of scholarship was paralleled in literature: J. E. Neale's novel *The Fall of Constantinople* (1857) represented the irenic concern of the Tractarians; but the writers of the decadence tended to cling to their over-simplified notions of Byzantine history. Symptomatic are such plays as Wills's *Claudian* (1884), of which Yeats writes in 1889; Sardou's *Theodora* translated into English in 1885; Michael Field's *Equal Love* (1896), high minded and highly coloured, which was published in the issue of *The Pageant* that contained a short story by Yeats: historical novels such as Frederic Harrison's *Theophano* (1904) and *Nicephorus* (1906) and, in France, Sar Péladan's play *Le Prince de Byzance* (1893).

In England, the circles which Yeats frequented were familiar with Byzantine art and specially with Ravenna. Burne-Jones visited the town in 1873 to see its 'heavenly churches', and himself designed mosaics: the revival of mosaic no less than cloisonnée, enamel with golden frames, another typically Byzantine mode of art, was part of that general 'revival' of the arts of design centring round Morris and his followers. F. G. Stephens lectured on Byzantine Art in Liverpool in 1878. Both Oscar Wilde and Arthur Symons visited and wrote about Ravenna. Although Wilde's *Ravenna* does not refer to the mosaics, elsewhere, in a passage in *The Decay of Lying,* which he had read to Yeats on a memorable Christmas, he writes of Byzantine art in terms which closely approach Yeats's own later conception of it:

> 'The whole history of the arts in Europe is the record of the struggle between Orientalism, with its frank rejection of imitation, its love of artistic convention, its dislike to the actual representation of any object in Nature, and our own imitative spirit. Wherever the former has been paramount, as in Byzantium, Sicily or Spain. . . . we have had beautiful and imaginative work in which the visible things of life are transmuted into artistic conventions and the things that life has not are invented and fashioned for her delight.'

Yeats's intimate friend, Arthur Symons, described Ravenna in his *Cities of Italy* (1907) and Constantinople in his *Cities* (1903), where there is an emphatic account of the impressiveness of Santa Sophia. Symons also has a poem of about the same date on the mosaics at Sant' Appollinare Nuovo. But, as Dr. Giorgio Melchiori observes in his brilliant analysis of the Byzantine poems, there is a passage in Yeats's early story *Rosa Alchemica* describing the mosaics of the apostles against their golden ground in the Battistero degli Ortodossi at Ravenna. The circular walk of the apostles round the dome recalls the 'perne in a gyre' of *Sailing to Byzantium.* The fact that these mosaics are in the dome, not along the walls, as at Sant' Apollinare would seem to relate them more firmly to *Byzantium,* (182, 183). The context in *Rosa Alchemica* includes a description of the Alchemists' refining fire 'and of a dancer under a dome of *flame-like* figures, which concludes in a half-dream'. Yet whatever Yeats may have gathered about Byzantium and its art from the literary field, it was his later historical reading and the visit to Sicily and Rome that conditioned his choice of Byzantium as a composite symbol.

Whatever Yeats had found and read about Byzantium in his English sources, in earlier years, had been fragmentary, and often trivial. His appropriation of Byzantium as symbol is a genuine conquest. The sort of feelings he came to have about Byzantium and Byzantine art and Santa Sophia were present in the early writers, in the eloquence of a Procopius or the dark poetic language (the phrase is Gibbon's) of Paul the Silentiary (whose accounts he must surely have found, perhaps in the Lethaby and Swainson); and could be found in a modern form, in 1911, unexpectedly perhaps, in Dalton's learned textbook:

> . . . Its forms do indeed evoke and quicken the sense of life, but it is a life elect and spiritual, and not the tumultuous flow of human existence. They are without the solidity of organisms which rejoice or suffer; they seem to need no sun and cast no shadow, emerging mysteriously from some radiance of their own. . . .

> It is greatest, it is most itself, when it frankly renounces nature; its highest level is perhaps attained where, as in the best mosaic, a grave schematic treatment is imposed, where no illusion of receding distance, no preoccupation with anatomy, is suffered to distract the eye from the central mystery of the symbol. The figures that ennoble these walls often seem independent of earth; they owe much of their grandeur to their detachment. They exert their compelling and almost magical power just because they stand on the very line between that which lives and that which is abstracted

In England it was in the early nineteen-twenties that the story began which has made Byzantine art so popular with the purveyors of those elaborate picture books which have taken the place of the early nineteenth-century annuals; and the story of the forces that made the reception of a non-naturalistic art eventually possible need not be rehearsed. Yeats was acting, as poets can, as antenna of his age: his crystallisation has become one of the meanings of Byzantium.

III Byzantine art becomes no less than a symbol for Art itself, for, in no other mode is the opposition between Art and Nature so strikingly expressed. The conventional forms of Byzantine mosaic seem to deny the nature from which they derive. Those images, in fact, were designed to express the Divine, the supernatural, the transcendent realm which opposes the flux of time and nature. The personal application of the symbol is intensified by Yeats's obsession with old age, change, decay and death, and with the wisdom that outlasts them. The symbol, then, expresses the permanence of the artist in the perfection of his artifices; but it contains more than this, for Byzantium, at its highest point, represented for Yeats a civilization in which all forms of thought, art and life interpenetrated one another, and where the artist 'spoke to the multitude and the few alike'. Byzantium is not only the city of perfected art. It is also a city dedicated to the Holy Wisdom, ruled by an Emperor, who himself is half divine, intermediary between God and Man, who sits in the throne of Solomon between the Lions and the Golden Tree. For this wisdom is the wisdom of both East and West: Byzantium was the meeting place of the two cultures that have formed the Western world. The whole city, with its great dome and its mosaics which defy nature and assert transcendence, and its theologically rooted and synthetic culture, can serve the poet as an image of the Heavenly City and the state of the soul when it is 'out of nature'.

Byzantium begins with the Emperor's dome. This, like the dome of Santa Sophia is Heaven, perfection, Eternity, a reversal of Shelley's 'dome of many-coloured glass', opposed to the natural world, the world of daylight, of passions, and flux, that is struck through by the liturgical gong, an intimation of a transcendent order. But the dome has other meanings. Dr Melchiori suggests that the dome is the equivalent of Blake's cosmic egg and the sphere, the perfect shape, and that Byzantium has succeeded to Blake's city of art, Golgonooza. The dome, an inclusive form, could be used as a symbol of the union of arts and activities which should characterize a good society, that favourite preoccupation of Yeats and his generation. A little magazine, to which Yeats contributed frequently between 1897 and 1900, was called *The Dome*, precisely because it was a 'union of the arts' magazine. In January 1899 the editor invited readers to contribute designs for a fantastic memorial college of arts in a ruined town; the winning design, not unnaturally included a dome (184). But in 1924 Yeats was to see the union of the arts manifested in another type of architecture. He associates the Stadhus of Stockholm with its stylized mosaics and his favourite art nouveau decoration with Byzantium. The Stadhus, he wrote, 'is decorated by many artists working in harmony with one another and with the design of the building as a whole, and yet all in seeming perfect freedom'. He refers to the mosaic-covered walls of the Golden Room (185), to the wrought iron work and bronzes 'naked as if they had come down from a Roman heaven . . . all that multitude and unity could hardly have been possible had not love of Stockholm and belief in its future so filled men of different minds, classes and occupations, that they almost attained the supreme miracle, the dream that haunted all religions'. This was to be closely echoed in Yeats's description of Byzantium in *A Vision.*

The Golden Tree with its Golden Bird in the poems exemplifies admirably the syncretistic nature of Yeats's Byzantine symbols. The golden bird is described as *set* on the golden bough, one of several ironic qualifications in the poem, confirmed by its role of keeping the drowsy Emperor awake. The bird is an automaton, like Andersen's mechanical bird with its cold songs that out-sing the nightingale; and Yeats may have been recalling Wilde's 'over our heads will float the Blue Bird singing of beautiful and impossible things, of things that are lovely and never happen, of things that are not and should be'. The similarities of cadence are striking and so too is the reversed effect: Yeats's bird can only sing of actual happenings in a phenomenal world, whose ecstatic absurdity is no longer possible in the Heaven of Art. The birds in the Throne of Solomon seemed to have sung through air being forced out of an air-tight compartment by the introduction of water (v. G. Brett, 'The Automata of the Byzantine Throne of Solomon', *Speculum,* 1954), and we show such an automaton from the twelfth century (186).

Yeats knew also from his reading in Strzygowski and in Goblet D'Alviella's *Migration of Symbols* (1894) – one of his sacred texts – of the stylized tree-pattern as it appears in near Eastern and Byzantine art - we show one of Strzygowski's illustrations (187) - and his authorities informed him that this could be identified with the Hebrew Tree of Life. Yeats chose to identify the Golden Tree of the Emperor with this all-important symbol, and it is tempting to think that he may have seen in the mosaic of the apse of San Clemente at Rome, with its cross springing from a stylized tree, yet another example of this form. He felt that he possessed sufficient historical evidence to justify such an identification and it was particularly important for him to do so, for in this way the image of Byzantium can be associated with the hermetic imagery of the Golden Dawn, the magical society in which Yeats was prominent for many years and whose rituals provided him with imagery that he never forgot. One of the fundamental symbols of the Order was in fact the Tree of Life, derived from Kabbalistic sources and expressed in geometrical form, as shown in our illustration (188). The Tree of Life or Minutum Mundum expresses the degrees of being and the way of ascent through the ten Sephiroth to the *Ain Soph,* that final wisdom which is the ground of being. The Golden Bird, and this once more is hermetic imagery, represents the purified soul. Byzantium in the second poem has moved out of history; it has become the City of the Dead and the poet is concerned with the fate of the soul after death. The method is still to add hermetic and pagan images to Byzantine images. The image and the shade of the second stanza have been related to the *ka* and *bai,* the impersonal double and the soul, often represented as bird-shaped, but with human head and often human arms, of Egyptian after-life (189, 190). Cumont's *After Life in Roman Paganism* (1922) – Yeats knew of Cumont's work – has a number of striking parallels of word and idea with *Byzantium:* the astrological sun and moon imagery, the journey of the departed soul across water, Hermes' role as summoner to re-birth and the distinction between 'image' and 'shade'. The cock of Hades is associated with Hermes as summoner, and this, as well as the dolphins, appears in Mrs Strong. The cock on sarcophagi was intended first as an emblem of protection against evil spirits, later became an image of re-birth and is frequently associated with the sun. In Regardie's *Golden Dawn,* Hermes' cock perches on the Tree of Life and it appears with the God in the Tarot pack (191).

A further example of this syncretistic method appears in the introduction of the Dolphin, who carries the souls of the dead. Yeats knew this detail in Mrs Strong, though in Angelo de Gubernatis' *Zoological Mythology* (1872) which he often used there is a more explicit account. Dolphins ridden by winged children are not unusual in Roman sarcophagi, and dolphins are found with peacocks in the decoration of San Vitale (192, 193, 194); dolphins with putti were a favourite motif with Renaissance sculptors and we show an example from a 15th century tomb (195). And when he went to

Sweden to receive the Nobel prize in 1923, Yeats, as Dr Melchiori reminds us, saw Carl Milles's *Sol Glitter,* a naiad riding a dolphin (196).

It is because Byzantium can include so much that Yeats can use it so powerfully; his synthetic or syncretistic method makes for the richness of the symbol; the sustained rhetoric guarantees its power. But of course this method, with the need it imposes for analysis of the kind sketched above, makes for difficulty and uncertainty – and of the second poem there is no completely acceptable account. Images of a life time are present; but there is no assurance that they still carry the meanings they had in earlier contexts. What is asserted with clarity, unforgettably, is Byzantium itself: and the stylisation of nature's violence and disorder.

D. J. Gordon / Ian Fletcher

176 La Zisa, Palermo, mosaic with trees and birds. Alinari.
177 San Clemente, Rome, mosaic in apse, crucifix with birds growing out of a stylized tree. Alinari.
178 San Clemente, Rome, mosaic in apse, crucifix with birds growing out of tree (detail). Alinari.
179 San Prassede, Rome, mosaic on tribune, apostles, angels, holy women. Alinari.
180 San Prassede, mosaic on tribune, apostles and angels. Alinari.
181 San Prassede, mosaic on vault of the Colonna chapel: the Redeemer with supporting angels. Alinari.
182 Battistero degli Ortodossi, Ravenna, mosaics in the dome. Alinari.
183 Battistero degli Ortodossi, mosaics in the dome. Alinari.
184 H. M. J. Close, a Memorial College, *The Dome.* March 1899, n.s.II,n.3.
185 Stockholm Stadhus, the Golden Chamber facing South.
186 Automata of Birds and Tree from a twelfth-century manuscript of Lamprecht.
187 Stylized Tree-Pattern, used for support for cross, Lemberg, Armenian Gospel of A.D. 1198, reproduced from Strzygowski's *Origin of Christian Church Art* (1923).
188 *'Minutum Mundum'. The Golden Dawn version of The Tree of Life. Diagram provided by Gerald Yorke Esq.*
189 *ka*, or double. Reproduced from H. Frankfort, *Kingship of the Gods,* Chicago, 1948.
190 *bai*, or purified shade. Reproduced from H. Frankfort, *Kingship of the Gods,* Chicago, 1948.
191 Hermes with cock, North Italian *Tarocchi,* late 15th century.
192 San Vitale, Ravenna, mosaic with dolphin ornament.
193 Dolphin bearing winged child, from Roman sarcophagus, 3rd cent. A.D.
194 Dolphins, sea-horses and erotes, from Roman sarcophagus, 3rd. cent. A.D. Photograph from the German Archaeological Institute, Rome.
195 Dolphins and putti, from Renaissance Tomb Siena. Alinari.
196 Sol Glitter by Carl Milles.

SYMBOLIC ART AND VISIONARY LANDSCAPE

'Art is Art because it is not Nature.'

SYMBOLIC ART

In this section, we do not aim at showing pictures that Yeats used as sources for his imagery. We aim simply to show the kind of painting he approved of. This is worth doing, because Yeats's taste in painting was conditioned by views which also deeply affected the nature of his poetry and because, in the complex, shifting and obscure history of the theory and practice of painting in this country, the tradition to which he belongs has been largely submerged and forgotten. Yeats was not isolated in his views; but the group to which he belonged was in its time isolated and moving against the main currents of taste (196a).

I Yeats grew up 'in all things Pre-Raphaelite'. John Butler Yeats in 1867 decided to give up the law and become a professional painter, and went to London to the art schools. It was at Hetherley's, a school more open to new influences than the Academy school (Samuel Butler was there at this time) that he met J. T. Nettleship (1841/1902), Edwin J. Ellis (1848/1916) and George M. Wilson (1848/ 1890). They formed a group so close that they called themselves 'the Brotherhood'. The reasons for this name are obvious. Pre-Raphaelite influences were dominant; and Nettleship was close to the Rossetti circle, and Rossetti, we know, so admired a drawing by Yeats that he invited him to Cheyne Walk. It is clear from letters of this period that Yeats even at the beginnings suffered from those uncertainties of purpose and doubts about his own art, which were to make it so difficult for him ever to carry a project to completion; and almost nothing of his Pre-Raphaelite period seems to survive, but we show a drawing 'Pippa', probably done about 1870 (197). From Yeats's letters to Todhunter (MSS. Reading University

Library), we know that he was illustrating Browning's poem at this time. In 1868 Nettleship published his *Essays on Robert Browning's Poetry,* a pioneering work. Like the older Pre-Raphaelites the whole group was passionately concerned with poetry. Ellis was a poet; we show the only drawing we have been able to trace of his, an allegory of time, fate and love, which illustrates a passage in his volume of verse *Seen in Three Days,* 1893 (198). George Wilson illustrated Shelley; we show a study of *Alastor* and *Asia* (199, 200), and the head of a young *Bacchante* from the collection of Dr John Todhunter (201).

In 1863 the first edition of Gilchrist's *Life of Blake* appeared, and in 1868 Swinburne's *Study.* These are symptomatic of that interest in Blake which never died, but was given new life and impetus in the Rossetti circle. John Butler Yeats's 'brotherhood' responded fully. About 1870, their Irish friend John Todhunter was giving a course of lectures on Blake at Alexandra College in Dublin. At the same time, Nettleship carried out a series of pencil drawings which have been known since in his family as 'The Blake Drawings'. This does not mean that they were illustrations of Blake, but that they were symbolic in the manner of Blake on topics of the Blake kind. Of those that remain, we do not know the subjects, or even whether they belong to one series; but clearly one theme is a struggle between good and evil in which a heroic figure is captive or engaged in battle, and is assisted by supernatural powers (202, 203, 204, 205, 206). It was in this circle and at this time that the roads were laid that led to W. B. Yeats's continuing concern with Blake: one of the threads that runs right through his work. He was to recall in a lecture given in Dublin in 1918 (reported in *The Irish Times,* April 15th) that when he was about sixteen – about 1881 – his father put into his hands Gilchrist's *Life of Blake* 'decorated with wonderful and mysterious pictures that no-one understood, and containing writings that many thought had no meaning at all'. These must have been some of Blake's illustrations to the Book of Job (207, 208). In 1887, John Butler Yeats, giving up the attempt to establish himself as a painter in Dublin, brought his family back to London, and next spring they took a house in Bedford Park, where they were to remain until the painter returned to Ireland for the last time in 1901. This return to Bedford Park meant that the young poet was to find the changed survivors of that 'brotherhood' of young men who had worked together in the sixties and early seventies. Nettleship was still working in London, Ellis had returned from Italy, and John Todhunter, who, though not of the brotherhood, had acted as friend and patron, was now living a few minutes walk away.

It is on consideration of what he found among these men and what had happened to them that W. B. Yeats bases the story of his alienation from his age. For him, what had happened to this group was exemplary. Yeats found in conversation and painting at Bedford Park what he most hated. The names he used to sum it up echo through the *Autobiographies:* Huxley and Tyndall, Jules Bastien-Lepage, Carolus Duran. With the positivism and rationalism of the philosophers, echoed in the discussion of his father's circle, he joins a school of painting which had replaced the Pre-Raphaelitism of J. B. Yeats and Nettleship. Not Manet, not Degas, but those two almost forgotten painters who were then at the height of their vogue. The 'grey photographic realism' of Bastien-Lepage (the words belong to an English art-historian of this period) developed out of Millet, had already had its effect on the 'Newlyn school' of painters (209); precisely in 1892 a book on him was published in London, including an essay by Walter Sickert on 'Modern Realism in Painting': an attack, it turns out, on Lepage and 'photographic realism' (this, however, in the name of Degas and impressionism). Carolus Duran's portraits were fashionable. His formula was developed out of Manet: a Manet simplified, palatable and easily imitated. 'Modern Realism': that was of course the trouble. It was the equivalent in art of Huxley and Tyndall, or of Ibsen. W. B. Yeats had come to England, nourished on Blake, Spenser and Shelley and already, in search for the religion that he demanded, in touch with Theosophical circles.

His father was painting those realistic portraits and Nettleship animals, observed in their natural habitat and duly hung in the Academy. Nettleship's last gestures in the direction of symbolic art had been his illustrations to the Pre-Raphaelite poet, Arthur O'Shaughnessy's *Epic of Women* (1870) (210, 211), and his contributions to Alicia Cholmondeley's *Emblems* (1875). Yeats was fascinated by the personality of Nettleship, which seemed of heroic mould, capable of huge efforts of suffering and recovery, and of the intensest religious feeling. Augustus John, who became his son-in-law, has an equally vivid memory of him and drew him with love (212). When Yeats found those early drawings by Nettleship in his studio he must have felt that he was restoring the true line. The work he most admired, *God creating Evil,* is said not to have survived, but it seems likely that *God with eyes turned upon his own glory,* which we show, is in fact this work (213). George Wilson, of whom less is known even than of the others, had died young in his native county, Aberdeenshire, after a nomadic life, chequered by ill-health, in 1890. He survives largely through the piety of Tod-hunter who discussed him in *The English Illustrated Magazine,*

August 1891 and who must have been responsible for the 1903 exhibition for which he wrote the catalogue. But there was one friend who had not abandoned his earlier interests. This was Edwin Ellis. Ellis, for the biographers of Yeats, has been an elusive figure. As late as 1936, Yeats admired his work sufficiently to include a poem of his in *The Oxford Book of Modern Verse*, but had completely lost touch with the circumstances of Ellis's later life. His father A. J. Ellis had been a wealthy mid-Victorian polymath; a mathematician who interested himself in philology; a familiar figure in the learned societies; a man probably whose real ability diffused itself and ended in the crankish. Edwin Ellis must have inherited enough money to allow him to live the life he chose. By 1837, he had returned from Perugia where he had a villa, and seems to have renewed his literary and artistic ambitions. He became a member of The Rhymers' Club in 1891; in 1892 he published his first collection of poems *Fate in Arcadia* and in 1894 his *Seen in Three Days,* where he attempts to mimic the effect in lithography of an illustrated book by Blake (214). He makes a spasmodic appearance as a reviewer of exhibitions in the new periodical *The Studio.* After the later 1890s he recedes again, publishes a small book on Blake in 1907, a handful of thin, miscellaneous works, married a second time, a German lady, and dies in Germany during the first world war. The most substantial of his works is that edition of the works of Blake with commentary, which he published in collaboration with Yeats in 1893. Yeats had found that Ellis had brooded for many years on Blake's symbolism; and it may well be that the final working out of his scheme and the appearance of the edition was due to Yeats's energy and enthusiasm.

II   It was now under the combined influence of Blake and of other religious, literary and hermetic studies, that Yeats began to enunciate a theory of the image as a vehicle and object of spiritual insight, the function of art being to mediate such images. Only those painters and poets whose work was open to this interpretation could be sympathetic to him, and from this position he never varied: his approaches in later years to other forms of modern art, which he rather uneasily knew to engage the contemporary imagination far more deeply than those with which he had spent his life, were tentative and hesitant. This meant that Yeats had to align himself with those who resented not so much the rather peripheral activities of Bedford Park, but the much stronger forces of the French Impressionists and their admirers in England and the new English painting done under their influence, mild though this was. For in the confused English scene Realism was one of the meanings given to Impressionism, an art, it was thought, for which subject – Yeats's principal concern – did not matter, and treatment was all. Yeats could associate himself with *Symboliste* poetic, so far as he knew it, as expounded by Arthur Symons, which carried implications for art, and seemed to confirm the position he was establishing for himself. And he could find, in London, heirs still lingering on of the Pre-Raphaelite and Morris traditions. In the circles to which Yeats gravitated towards 1890 we can see the influence of such movements. He found his way to 20 Fitzroy Street, that 'nest of decayed Preraphaelites' according to Augustus John who knew it. This Fitzroy 'colony' was the headquarters of the Century Guild which had been founded in 1882. Its organ was *The Century Guild Hobby Horse* edited effectively by Herbert Horne, with assistance from A. H. Mackmurdo and Selwyn Image. Its aim was Morris's aim, the association of artists in all fields. And here Yeats could find, to isolate two topics, admiration for Blake and polemic against Naturalism. Thus the 1888 volume (215) has reproductions of three of Blake's Virgil woodcuts and an attack by Image on 'Naturalism' (which means 'Realism') in painting as exemplified in a pamphlet by the secretary of the New English Art Club, which had been founded in 1886, to be a kind of *Salon des Refusés,* a home for the new painting. Image quotes this sentence: 'Art is only an accurate reflection of natural appearances', so that he can reply 'that seems precisely what Art is not'. Such a view, he thinks, belongs to science; to Art, Nature 'is a storehouse of raw material, of symbols. . . .' It was in Arthur Symons's and Beardsley's *Savoy* that Yeats was able to publish his articles on Blake's illustrations to *The Divine Comedy,* in which he claims Blake as precursor of the modern *Symboliste* movement, 'the first great *Symboliste* of modern times and the first of any time to preach the indissoluble marriage of all great art with symbol'. And here is Yeats's diagram of the present situation:

> 'The recoil from scientific naturalism has created in our day the movement the French call *Symboliste,* which, beginning with the memorable 'Axel', by Villiers de l'Isle Adam, has added to drama a new kind of romance, at once ecstatic and picturesque, in the works of M. Maeterlinck; and beginning with certain pictures of the Pre-Raphaelites, and of Mr Watts and Mr Burne-Jones, has brought into art a new and subtle inspiration' (216).

We can see how Yeats's history of contemporary art and his repertory of admired artists is being built up, but certain steps have to be taken before, becoming more exotic in the process, it reaches the form which is to last him. Here is a late account of it:

'The great myth-makers and mask-makers, the men of aristocratic mind, Blake, Ingres in the *Perseus,* Puvis de Chavannes, Rossetti before 1870, Watts when least a moralist, Gustave Moreau at all times, Calvert in the woodcuts, the Charles Ricketts of *The Danaides,* and of the earlier illustrations of *The Sphinx, . . .'*.

Yeats wrote this in *The Bounty of Sweden* in 1925. At this point we may consider the intervention of Charles Ricketts (1866/1931) in the formation of Yeats's taste. At the end of his life, broadcasting on Modern Poetry in 1936, we find Yeats saying:

'When I think of the Rhymers' Club and grow weary of those luckless men, I think of another circle that was in full agreement. It gathered round Charles Ricketts, one of the greatest connoisseurs of any age, an artist whose woodcuts prolonged the inspiration of Rossetti, whose paintings mirrored the rich colouring of Delacroix. When we studied his art we studied our double.'

Yeats first met Ricketts and his friend C. H. Shannon (217, 218) in the early 90s through the Fitzroy group, but only became intimate with Ricketts towards the end of the decade. By this time Ricketts had made several reputations. It has been claimed that his earlier work in typography was more important than Morris's, for he worked through commercial printers and publishers. John Gray's *Silverpoints* (1893), entirely designed by him, and Wilde's *Sphinx* (1894) (219, 220), are among the most perfect and wholly characteristic productions of the 1890s. In 1896, he set up his own press, The Vale Press. Between 1889 and 1897 he and Shannon brought out their lavish magazine *The Dial* (221), largely devoted to their own work with some assistance from other members of their circle, such as Sturge Moore – for whom Yeats was never to lose admiration. Between 1896 and 1897 Shannon edited with Gleeson White *The Pageant;* and Ricketts certainly had a large share in it. Almost certainly it was Ricketts – 'my mentor in so many things' – who was responsible for adding Ingres and Delacroix, Puvis and Moreau to Yeats's repertory. Yeats contributed in 1896 one of the stories that was to appear in *The Secret Rose* (he was with Verlaine and Maeterlinck and many English friends); and the illustrations to the two volumes are an anthology of symbolist painting, illustrating the history Yeats had already sketched (222, 223). In 1896, we have Rossetti, the Preraphaelite Millais, Watts, Burne-Jones, Whistler, Ricketts's *Oedipus* and *Psyche,* and a Botticelli allegory. In 1897, we have two Rossettis,

Burne-Jones, Watts, three Moreaus: *Hercules and the Hydra, The Apparition, The Sphinx;* and *Young Girls by the Sea* and *Young Girls and Death* by Puvis de Chavannes. There is also an article on Gustave Moreau by Gleeson White, in which he protests against the English habit of calling Moreau 'the French Burne-Jones'. Ingres and Delacroix, to complete Yeats's list, were masters followed by Ricketts in his own art. He had been among the earliest admirers of Moreau and Puvis de Chavannes, and Moreau could be very neatly accommodated to Yeats's history of symbolist art. They were French representatives of *Symbolisme* in painting. The reputation of Puvis's idyllic landscapes and mythologies sacred and profane, and of Moreau's exotic and incrusted enigmas had been built by French men of letters looking, like Yeats, for a symbolic art: their daylight and nocturnal dreams. Moreau's *L'Apparition* had been shown in London in 1877 at the opening of the new Grosvenor Galleries when Burne-Jones exhibited publicly for the first time.

To illustrate Yeats's history of modern symbolic art, we may start with the familiar allegories of Burne-Jones. We show two sketches, companion pieces, for the *Venus Concordia* and *Venus Discordia* (224, 225) and photographs of three famous pieces *Quia Multum Amavit, Love Leading the Pilgrim* and *The Golden Stair* (226, 227, 228). We then show some of the allegories of G. F. Watts. Watts was an oddly isolated figure even in his own time. His allegories, whatever we may like to think now, did not appeal simply to a late Victorian taste for visual platitude. Yeats admits him 'when least a moralist', and we show *The Curse of Cain* and *The Court of Death* (229, 230); also photographs of his *Psyche, Love and Life* and *Hope* (231, 232, 233) because these last three were singled out by Arthur Symons for special praise as being true symbolical pictures, revealing 'an unfaltering life of the soul'. Symons is trying to make the distinction – which was all important for Yeats – between Allegory and Symbol. And according to Symons the *Mammon* (234), a photograph of which we also show, is bad because the idea is not implicit in the lines of the composition, but seems extrinsic to the painting, which therefore falls into the class of allegory. But, says Symons: 'whenever he is fully himself . . . there is no conflict between form and meaning, the symbol is more than allegory, the picture is more than a painted poem'.

In the work of Puvis de Chavannes it was a tone and a feeling that appealed. Charles Ricketts found in his *La Toilette* (235) 'a primeval candour of vision and emotion' and held him to be the most original designer of landscape 'since Rembrandt'; landscape firmly designed but catching delicate and passing moments and seasons and always associated with man 'as worker or dreamer', nobly seen.

What they found in these figures in landscapes – a saint at prayer among the trees, watched by country people, or girls playing unaware of death, or a fisherman by the sea, or solemn mythological beings – was the transfiguration of man through an innocent vision (236, 237, 238). Gustave Moreau's appeal lay in his repertory of images, exotic, sinister in colour and suggestion, a mixed pantheon of divinities. He liked to create enigmas and was given to explaining them in prose-poems. From these we chose subjects which particularly interested Yeats, like *Salome* (239), or *Leda* (240), or *Ladies and Unicorns* (241, 242); we know that a reproduction of one such group hung for many years in Yeats's room and according to him represented 'mystery'. We show two costume designs for *Sappho* (245) and two versions of *Oedipus and the Sphinx* (243, 244). Of these one is monochrome, and a third attempt at this very unusual rendering of the subject appeared in *The Pageant* in 1897. To show how unusual, there is Ingres' *Oedipus and the Sphinx* (246). A pen drawing by Charles Ricketts (247) shows him for his Oedipus following the composition of Ingres, but the accessories and the Sphinx belong to the world of Moreau; it is an encounter between a young man and a Fatal Woman; the riddle, if there is a riddle, is not the classical one. A later drawing by Ricketts for another illustrated edition of Wilde's *Sphinx* (1910), a study for the Sphinx as lover of the winged Assyrian God, shows clearly a very direct dependence on Moreau's *Oedipus* with its scheme of the tiny Sphinx clutching the semi-nude male figure (248).

III If the symbol partakes of the divine order and from that derives its power and if the divine order is accessible to the gifted through trance or vision, then the most powerful of all symbols must be those which are the direct records of visions given in such states. So the argument can run. It can lead the symbolist into dangerous places. If you are looking for symbols, you are certain to find them. And there was in the history sketched by Yeats the dangerous precedent of Blake. Just how far such an argument could lead Yeats, we can see by studying two odd episodes in his life; they also show that he was not really, finally, deceived.

In that strange house which held the Dublin Theosophists, Yeats met, towards the end of the 1880s, a tall girl, with red-gold hair and a beautiful voice. Her name was Althea Gyles (1868/1949). She had left home to study art. Her family was old and distinguished, and a full story of her relationship with them we do not know. But one of the Theosophists had rescued her from semi-starvation. In the early nineties, Althea Gyles came to London to continue her studies at Pedder's and the Slade; by the middle of the decade, she had become a member of the Order of the Golden Dawn, probably through Yeats. In 1897 Yeats had her do the cover design for his *The Secret Rose* (249). Her design shows the Tree of Life with a rose at its centre and two heads, male and female, involved in its intricate branches, clasping hands and kissing above the central Tudor Rose. In December 1898, Yeats published an essay on her work, 'A Symbolic Artist and the coming of Symbolic Art' in *The Dome.* Here, as in his 1896 essay on the Blake illustrations in the *Savoy,* Yeats hails the advent of a new manner in the art of the world. Miss Gyles's work is related to Whistler's and Beardsley's and to Charles Ricketts, and to the new French and Irish writers. Everywhere, he finds that 'a passion for symbol has taken the place of the old interest in life'. The marks of the new art are an absence of interest in 'subject' and a concern for pattern and rhythm. What Yeats means by 'life' we can see from his choice of an artist to represent those who are still interested in it. He chooses Degas, and argues that interest in life now must mean cynicism. Yeats was almost compelled to choose Degas, for Degas, more than any other painter, stood in England for the new 'Impressionist' or 'Realist' art. In 1893, the exhibition of Degas' *Au Café* – exhibited under the title of *L'Absinthe* – had provoked the crisis, the headlong battle about 'Realism' and the 'subject' in painting (250). This we may take as the exemplary episode in the history of English opinion in this period. Yeats could not have avoided its echoes. And he has rather changed his ground on the question of the 'subject'. The disappearance of the 'subject' is no longer a sign of a concern with realism; it is a sign of the coming of symbolism.

Four drawings by Miss Gyles are illustrated in *The Dome: Noah's Raven, The Knight upon the Grave of His Lady, Deirdre* and *Lilith* (251, 252, 253). From Yeats's correspondence we gather that the commentary here offered on these drawings was based on what the artist herself said to him – in response to a telegram – but clarified and elaborated by him. The Raven, equated with man's will, has emerged from the Ark, man's personality, to find out whether the Rose is anywhere above the flood of the five senses. 'He has found it, but is returning with it to the ark that the soul of man may sink into the ideal and pass away; but the sea-nymphs, the spirits of the senses, have bribed him with a ring taken from the treasures of the kings of the world, a ring that gives the mastery of the world, and he has given them the Rose. Henceforth man will seek for the ideal in the flesh, and the flesh will be full of illusive beauty, and the spiritual beauty will be far away.' Of *The Knight,* Yeats says that 'there is a heart in the bulb of every hyacinth to personify the awakening of the soul and of love out of the grave'. *Lilith,* 'the ever-changing phantasy of passion, rooted in neither good nor evil, half crawls upon the ground, like a serpent before the great serpent of the world, her guardian and her shadow ... Adam, and things to come, are reflected on the wings of a serpent. ... A place shaped like a heart is full of thorns and roses'. He had, it is fair to remember, reservations about the composition of the *Lilith.* (Whatever his reservations, Yeats thought well enough of Miss Gyles's work – or was sufficiently interested in her personality and sufficiently sorry for her – to commission her to do the cover design for the *Poems* of 1899 (254) and of *The Wind among the Reeds* of that same year.) Her design for the *Poems* shows the cross emblazoned with the rose, surrounded with swirling lines and drifting petals. On the spine is a face grafted to a tree and hands clutching at the petals. This imagery is clearly hermetic, and relates to the numerous rose poems Miss Gyles was writing at that time, and of course to the design for *The Secret Rose;* and to the unpublished portrait drawing of Yeats showing the rose and the floating petal; and presumably also, to Horton's rose drawing, which we show later.

Althea Gyles's life grew stranger and more tragic. She seems to have come to work for Leonard Smithers about 1899. She became involved in the extraordinary magical duel that took place between Yeats and Aleister Crowley, MacGregor Mathers's emissary, for control of the Golden Dawn. Crowley published a short story *At the Fork of the Road* in which he claimed that she acted for Yeats in this, and that through his own counter-magic she became Smithers's mistress. At any rate Miss Gyles suffered a break-down about 1901 and refused to do any more line-drawing. Her illustrations, done for Smithers, to Wilde's *Harlot's House,* seem to be the last of her work in this field (255).

She seems to have moved away from the centres of action, devoting herself to literature – there are some minor publications – and to various religious cults. We hear of her returning to London between the two wars, moving from rented room to rented room, casting horoscopes and collecting antiques of doubtful value. Her family was anxious to help her, but she refused all their offers. She had friends – among them Clifford Bax and Eleanor Farjeon; and was capable of inspiring devotion. There is a portrait of her in her middle years in Faith Compton Mackenzie's novel *Tatting* (1957). She may well have been one of those figures familiar, and wondered at, whom one used to see in the reading room of the British Museum.

In that same year 1898 Yeats contributed an introduction to W. T. Horton's *Book of Images* (256, 257). Yeats's introduction is far more ambitious than his article on Althea Gyles, and full of doctrine. Its basis is the distinction *via* Blake between Allegory and Symbol; on the symbol as in effect magical, entangling 'in complex colours and forms a part of the divine essence'; on the relationship between the symbols or orders of symbols created by the artist and the images that come to the visionary. And he sets up his repertory:

> 'Wagner's dramas, Keats's odes, Blake's pictures and poems, Calvert's pictures, Rossetti's pictures, Villiers de l'Isle Adam's plays, and the black-and-white art of M. Hermann, Mr Beardsley, Mr Ricketts, and Mr Horton, and the lithographs of Mr Shannon, and the pictures of Mr Whistler, and the plays of M. Maeterlinck, and the poetry of Verlaine.'

Horton's images interest Yeats because they are records of things received in actual state of vision. He speaks of Horton as being a disciple of 'The Brotherhood of the New Life' – which 'finds the way to God in waking dreams'. Some copies of the book have a publisher's slip apologising to the Brotherhood for this reference: the waking dreams are to be taken as 'purely personal', the Brotherhood claiming 'to be practical rather than visionary'.

Such a note is perhaps characteristic of Horton's life. In 1896 he had contributed drawings to *The Savoy* – possibly through an acquaintance with Beardsley. At that time he was thirty-two; he had inherited some money; had travelled; been trained as an architect, attempted to set up a practice, attempted literature and art. This was his first success, and he never again came so close to acceptance in the literary and artistic world. And in 1896 we have the first known letter addressed to him by Yeats. (The University of Reading possesses transcripts of Yeats's letters; the originals have not been traced). This is about Horton's initiation into the Order of the Golden Dawn, which, however, he was not to find satisfactory. His life was to be devoted to the search for direct contact with the supernatural world; to the cultivation of vision, to astrology and spiritualism. He moved restlessly between London and Brighton. His drawings are to be found in the corners of the periodicals and illustrating trivial jokes in the new cheap weekly papers. His most substantial publication is *The Way of the Soul,* an emblem book published in 1910, though perhaps written in the late '90s (258). Solitude seems to be the note of his life, and intransigence. The drama of his later years lies in his relationship with Audrey Locke until her death in 1916. Yeats's letters show patience and kindness and a refusal to take offence with a man who must have been easily offended and difficult to deal with, and he put Horton among the figures he remembers in *All Souls Night.*

Aubrey Beardsley remarked of Horton that he 'had a sort of a kind of talent'. It is difficult to better the judgement. To go through the hundreds of drawings by Horton in the University of Reading collection or in Bodley is not inspiriting. Yeats was not really deceived. His reservations are already in the conclusion of his introduction when he refers to the weakness of Horton's drawing and 'the immaturity of his art'. And he was to tell Horton very firmly in his letters about his weakness as poet and artist. Yeats knew and told Horton that he had better learn his craft and 'force himself to study from the life and nature in every form'. He omitted the last section of his introduction and all mention of Horton's name when he reprinted it as an essay on *Symbolism in Art in Ideas of Good and Evil* (1903); and in 1915 Horton was still offended by this and Yeats was still refusing to allow Horton to quarrel with him.

'Vision' was certainly not enough when its results were as thin and iconographically banal as those black-and-white drawings that we find in *The Book of Images* or illustrating some kind of moral pilgrimage or Blakeian cosmology (259, 260, 261); and whatever the Rose stood for its power is hardly indicated in the nursery landscape Horton provides for it (262). He tried his hand at illustration and we show a preparatory drawing for one of Poe's tales *The Fall of the House of Usher* (263). And there are totally conventional nursery-rhyme pictures (264). But he is capable of a distinctly less conventional note, and nursery rhymes seem to have brought this out. In the two illustrations for Jack and Jill (265) it is pretty obviously mediated through Beardsley's clowns or Pierrots; but in the coloured drawings for his child's book *The Book of Grig* (1900), there is an original suggestion of the monstrous, not particularly suitable for children, and in such a drawing as *Little Bo-peep has found her sheep* (266), there is a perversion of the formula that is perhaps more horrid than he intended. This feeling finds its way into his versions of popular proverbs, a combination of a sort of *Tit-Bits* facetiousness with almost surrealist forms (267). When he tried to comment directly on society as in, for example, *A Meeting of the Board* (268) he does not seem very happy. He is more successful in creating monsters as emblems of contemporary vices (269, 270). And even a purely comic monster like his *Sea Serpent* has perhaps something to be said for it (271). All of Horton's work shows a depressing gap between ambition and execution, between imagination and the demands made on it. In the mass it witnesses to a persistence that could never come to anything. The saddest of all in the poverty of their imagery are his later visionary records in crayon, records of his most important experiences, sometimes marked with the appropriate astrological symbols or with such a detail as 'after dreams of her' (272, 273, 274). When Miss Locke died Yeats wrote to Horton: 'She had talent, and great charm and must have been much interwoven in your thought . . . the dead are not far from us . . . they cling in some strange way to what is most deep and still within us'. When Horton tried to record this in a self-portrait showing the spiritual presence of the lady, the year after her death, the inadequacy of feeling and will to produce the image is almost desperately apparent (275). Yeats was to remember of Horton in *All Souls Night* that he had:

> 'loved strange thought
> And knew that sweet extremity of pride
> That's called platonic love,
> And that to such a pitch of passion wrought
> Nothing could bring him, when his lady died,
> Anodyne for his love.
> Words were but wasted breath;
> One dear hope had he:
> The inclemency
> Of that or the next winter would be death.'

VISIONARY LANDSCAPE

> 'Calvert and Wilson, Blake and Claude,
> Prepared a rest for the people of God,
> Palmer's phrase, but after that
> Confusion fell upon our thought.'

IV This account of Yeats and the visual arts of his time began with Blake, and it is to Blake that we must return to tell the story of one special preoccupation. This is what is called 'visionary landscape'. The assumption here is that the world as we see it is only a shadow of a glorified eternal world, to which the visionary imagination has access – the imagination of the poet or painter, for to painters in this tradition the two arts were one. The notion of an art of 'visionary landscape' was consciously elaborated by the followers of Blake in England, notably by Samuel Palmer (1805/1881) and Edward Calvert (1799/1883). These painters derived their inspiration directly from Blake's illustrations for Thornton's *Virgil*. This was an edition of the *Pastorals* intended to be used in schools, very lavishly illustrated, by various hands. Blake contributed – as well as some engravings of portraits – twenty woodcuts, seventeen of which he cut himself (276).

'Nature has properties' wrote Palmer 'and when they are brought out the picture must be most elaborate and full of matter even if only one subject be represented, yet it will be most simple of style, and be what would have pleased men in the early ages, when poetry was at its acme, and yet men lived in a simple, pastoral way'. The Thornton illustrations were to him his 'heart's delight' (his son records that he spoke of them as 'perhaps the most intense gems of bucolic sentiment in the whole range of art'); and here is the passage which Yeats recalled in his poem:

> 'I sat down with Mr Blake's Thornton's *Virgil* woodcuts before me, thinking to give to their merits my feeble testimony. I happened first to think of their sentiment. They are visions of little dells, and nooks, and corners of Paradise; models of the exquisitest patch of intense poetry. I thought of their light and shade, and looking upon them I found no word to describe it. Intense depth, solemnity, and vivid brilliancy only coldly and partially described them. There is in all such a mystic and dreamy glimmer as penetrates and kindles the inmost soul, and gives complete and unreserved delight, unlike the gaudy daylight of this world. They are like all that wonderful artist's works the drawing aside of the fleshly curtain, and the glimpse which all the most holy, studious saints and sages have enjoyed, of that rest which remaineth to the people of God.'

In this tradition, behind Blake, Palmer sees Poussin and Claude, 'the greatest landscape painter who ever lived', who 're-opened upon canvas the vistas of Eden', whose *Enchanted Castle* is 'that divinest of landscapes' (277); who is principally to be admired, not for his truth of colour or the gold of his sunshine, but for 'that

Golden Age into which poetic minds are thrown back, on first sight of one of his genuine *uncleaned* pictures'. To Claude Yeats has added Richard Wilson, for his 'ideal landscapes' (278). And there were the poets themselves, the Virgil of the eclogues and the Milton of *L'Allegro* and *Il Penseroso*. For many years Palmer worked, in love and meditation, towards illustrations of Milton's minor poems and an illustrated *Eclogues,* with his own paraphrases; the two volumes were published, the *Virgil* in 1883, the *Milton* in 1889 by his son, who also published, in 1892, the *Life and Letters* which Yeats read, and from which we have been quoting (279, 280, 281, 282). One of these etchings, *The Lonely Tower* from *Il Penseroso* was among Yeats's most important symbols; and it was from these works that Yeats chose to illustrate Palmer's art in the lecture on 'William Blake and his School' which he prepared in 1918 – an exception is Palmer's *Christmas,* an illustration of the sonnet by Bampfylde (283, 284, 285).

Calvert shared with Palmer his discipleship to Blake, his devotion to pastoral painting, his conviction that painting and poetry are one – 'Poetic art, expressing itself by verse, by marble, or by picture is one of man's loftiest pursuits', Palmer had said – and his culti-vation, in retirement, of the life of meditation. He said 'a good poem, whether painted or written, whether large or small, should represent the simplicity of a beautiful life'. Colour is not necessary for 'painted poesy', 'black and white were enough – the very attempt to express the confession of love, were fulfilment sufficient'. Blake's *Virgil* woodcuts are his instance: a sacramental universe his meaning (286, 287, 288).

It is doubtful whether Palmer and Calvert were ever really forgotten, though they moved, in their long secluded lives, away from the public world. It is certain that their work was known and admired by the Rossetti circle; and Palmer's later work as etcher and illustrator was known and praised. In 1882, the year after his father's death, Palmer's son published a memoir of him to accompany a catalogue of the retrospective exhibition of his work put on by the Fine Art Society, in 1881: a sketch to be followed by his *Life and Letters* in 1892. In 1893 a son of Calvert's published his *Memoir* of his father (289). In that year we hear of Ricketts and Shannon visiting Burlington House and being 'greatly moved' by six designs in sepia by Palmer. These belonged to 1825, the 'visionary years' period acclaimed by contemporary critics (290); they conveyed their excite-ment to Sturge Moore, who never forgot it and recalled the moment many years later. And there is in the nineties a periodical literature on both artists, stimulated, presumably, by the general revival of interest in book illustration which also prompted the study of Blake's wood-cuts.

It was inevitable, from his absorption in Blake, his circle of friends, and the periodicals he read, that Yeats should encounter in the nineties the work of Palmer and Calvert. In 1898, in the preface to *A Book of Images* he wrote of Calvert being like Blake or Wagner a symbolist, but a 'fragmentary symbolist',

> ' for while he evokes in his persons and his landscapes an infinite emotion, a perfected emotion, a part of the Divine Essence he does not set his symbols in the great procession as Blake would have him. . . .'

And in the same year, in his essay on Althea Gyles he quotes from Palmer's *Life*.

So marked was the impression Calvert made – his mind was more curious and speculative than Palmer's – that Yeats at the turn of the century planned a short monograph on him, to be published by the Unicorn Press, one of a series to which a number of his friends contributed: advertisements can be seen in *The Dome,* also published by the Unicorn Press. No notes for this, however, seem to have survived. (It may not be mere coincidence that in 1897 Ricketts had published two of Calvert's woodcuts in *The Pageant,* singling them out for praise.) When Yeats was working on his historical studies, preparatory to *A Vision,* we find a renewed interest in the two artists. In 1918 he writes of how his table in Bodley was covered with their work. It has been shown that *In Memory of Major Robert Gregory* owes something to Palmer's prose; and it is possible that one of the reasons for turning to Calvert again was Calvert's attempt to elaborate a cyclic theory of history, giving to each phase as symbol the name of a Greek God.

Palmer and Calvert were close to Yeats's mind when he thought of Robert Gregory, for in Robert Gregory as landscape painter he saw an heir to their tradition. In his *Observer* 'appreciation' he explicitly relates Gregory to that great line:

> 'A man of letters may perhaps find in work such as this, or in old Chinese painting, in the woodcuts and etchings of Calvert and Palmer, in Blake's woodcuts to Thornton's Virgil, in the

landscape background to Mr Ricketts' 'Wise and Foolish Virgins', something that he does not find in the great modern masters, and that he cares for deeply. Is it merely that these men share certain moods with great lyric poetry, with, let us say, the 'Leech Gatherer' of Wordsworth; or that their moods, unlike those of men with more objective curiosity, are a part of the traditional expression of the soul.'

In a letter Yeats speaks of the combination of 'majesty', 'austerity', and 'sweetness' in Gregory's painting and says that no contemporary landscape had moved him so much, 'except perhaps a certain landscape by Innes, from which he had learnt a great deal'. This is J. D. Innes, that painter of such conspicuous promise who died so tragically young in 1914, when he was twenty-seven. He was a friend of Gregory's and stayed at Coole; and together with Gregory's *Orpheus* (291) a decorative painting, in a style derived from the late Pre-Raphaelites (and from one of their main sources, fifteenth-century Italian engravings) and two of his low toned paintings of Coole Lake (292, 293), we show five landscapes by Innes: *The Waterfall,* 1910, *The Mountain Pool,* 1911, *Seaton Mountains,* 1912, *The Van Pool,* 1912, and *By the Lake, Arenig,* about 1913 (294, 295, 296, 297, 298). The relationship with Gregory's work is apparent; and so are lessons which Augustus John, Innes's devoted friend, avowedly learnt from him.

D. J. Gordon / Ian Fletcher

196a *'Head of a Young Man' by W. B. Yeats; water-colour drawing in the National Gallery of Ireland, Dublin.*

197 *Pippa Passes* **by J. B. Yeats, c1870; drawing in the National Gallery of Ireland, Dublin. Photograph by Sparkes.**

198 *An Allegory of Time, Fate and Love* by E. J. Ellis, from *Seen in Three Days*, 1894. Photograph from original drawing in the University of Reading collection.

199 *Alastor* by George Wilson.

200 *Asia* by George Wilson. Photographs 199 and 200 by John Freeman from autotypes in the Victoria and Albert Museum.

201 *'Head of a Bacchante' by George Wilson; chalk drawing from Dr J. Todhunter's collection, now in the University of Reading.*

202 ⎫
203 │ Five drawings 'inspired by Blake' by J. T. Nettleship, c1870.
204 ⎬ Photographs from originals in the possession of the University
205 │ of Reading. (Pl. 27 and 28).
206 ⎭

207 **Illustrations for** *The Book of Job* **by William Blake, 1825; in the British Museum, and copy of book in the Whitworth Art Gallery, University of Manchester.**

208 *'Life of William Blake' by A. Gilchrist, 1863; Vols. I and II, in the Whitworth Art Gallery, University of Manchester.*

209 *'Study for The Potato Gatherers' by J. Bastien-Lepage; crayon drawing in the Whitworth Art Gallery, University of Manchester.*

210 and 211 Frontispiece and illustration by J. T. Nettleship for *An Epic of Women*, 1870, by A. O'Shaughnessy.

212 *J. T. Nettleship* by Augustus John, c1900; pencil drawing in the collection of The Misses Nettleship.

213 *God with eyes turned upon his own glory* by J. T. Nettleship, c1869, (more probably *God creating evil*). Reproduced from a photograph in Thomas Wright's *Life of John Payne* (1919).

214 *Pages from ' Seen in Three Days ' by E. J. Ellis, 1894; in the University of Reading collection.*

215 *'The Century Guild Hobby Horse', Vol. III, 1888; in the University of Reading collection.*

216 *'The Savoy', Vol. II, 1896; in the University of Reading collection.*

217 *'Charles Ricketts' by C. H. Shannon, 1899; chalk drawing in The National Portrait Gallery, London.*

218 *' Self-portrait' by C. H. Shannon; oil painting in The National Portrait Gallery, London.*

219 Title page of Oscar Wilde's, *The Sphinx* by C. Ricketts, 1894.

220 *Oscar Wilde's 'The Sphinx', designed by C. Ricketts, 1894; in the University of Reading collection.*

221 *'The Dial', No. 1, 1889, edited by C. Ricketts and C. H. Shannon; in the University of Reading collection.*

222 *'The Pageant', 1896, edited by C. H. Shannon and T. W. Gleeson White; in the University of Reading collection.*

223 *'The Pageant', 1897; in the University of Reading collection.*

224 *'Venus Concordia' by Sir Edward Burne-Jones, 1871; pencil drawing in the Whitworth Art Gallery, University of Manchester.*

225 *'Venus Discordia' by Sir Edward Burne-Jones; pencil drawing in the Whitworth Art Gallery, University of Manchester.*

226 *The Golden Stair* by Sir Edward Burne-Jones, 1880; oil painting in the Tate Gallery.

227 *Love leading the Pilgrim* by Sir Edward Burne-Jones, 1887; oil painting in the Tate Gallery.

228 *Quia Multum Amavit* by Sir Edward Burne-Jones, 1874; oil painting in the Tate Gallery.

229 *'The Curse of Cain' by G. F. Watts; oil painting in the Norwich Museums collection.*

230 *'The Court of Death' by G. F. Watts; oil painting in the Norwich Museums collection. (Pl. 26).*

231 *Psyche* by G. F. Watts; oil painting in the Tate Gallery.

232 *Love and Life* by G. F. Watts, 1885; oil painting in the Tate Gallery.

233 *Hope* by G. F. Watts, 1885; oil painting in the Tate Gallery.

234 *Mammon* by G. F. Watts; oil painting in the Tate Gallery.

235 *La Toilette* by Puvis de Chavannes; oil painting in the National Gallery, London.

236 *'S. Geneviève at prayer', lithograph by Puvis de Chavannes; in the collection of Professor D. J. Gordon.*

237* *'A Study for Le Travail' by Puvis de Chavannes, c1863; red and black chalk drawing in the Fitzwilliam Museum, Cambridge.*

238 *'Solitude' by Puvis de Chavannes; pastel drawing in the Whitworth Art Gallery, University of Manchester.*

H

239 *Salome* by Gustave Moreau; oil painting in the Musée Gustave Moreau, Paris. Photo Bulloz.

240 *Leda* by Gustave Moreau; oil painting in the Musée Gustave Moreau, Paris. Photo Bulloz.

241 *Ladies with Unicorns* by Gustave Moreau; oil painting in the Musée Gustave Moreau, Paris. Photo Bulloz.

242 *Lady with Unicorns* by Gustave Moreau; oil painting in the Musée Gustave Moreau, Paris. Photo Bulloz.

243 *Oedipus and the Sphinx* by Gustave Moreau; oil painting in the Musée Gustave Moreau, Paris. Photo Bulloz.

244 *Oedipus and the Sphinx* by Gustave Moreau; oil painting in the Musée Gustave Moreau, Paris. Photo Bulloz.

245* *'Two Costume Designs for Sappho' by Gustave Moreau; pencil and black chalk drawing in the Fitzwilliam Museum, Cambridge.*

246 *Oedipus and the Sphinx* by T. A. D. Ingres, c1808; oil painting in the National Gallery, London.

247 *Oedipus and the Sphinx* by C. Ricketts; pen drawing formerly in the possession of Sir William Rothenstein and from reproduction in *Sturge Moore, Charles Ricketts,* 1933.

248 *The Assyrian God* by C. Ricketts; preparatory drawing for the second series of illustrations for Wilde's *Sphinx* (1910) formerly in the possession of C. H. Shannon and from reproduction in *Sturge Moore, Charles Ricketts,* 1933.

249 W. B. Yeats's *The Secret Rose,* 1897; cover design by Althea Gyles.

250 *Au Café* (also known as *L'Absinthe)* by Edgar Degas; oil painting in The Louvre, Paris.

251 *Noah's Raven* by Althea Gyles; illustration from *The Dome,* Vol. I, No. 3, December 1898.

252 *The Knight upon The Grave of His Lady* by Althea Gyles; illustration from *The Dome,* Vol. I, No. 3, December 1898.

253 *Lilith* by Althea Gyles; illustration from *The Dome,* Vol. I, No. 3, December 1898.

254 *Poems* by W. B. Yeats, 1899; cover design by Althea Gyles.

255 *The Dead are dancing with the Dead* by Althea Gyles; illustration for *The Harlot's House* by Oscar Wilde, privately printed for Leonard Smithers, Mathurin Press, 1904.

256 *W. T. Horton;* portrait photograph by Edmund Wheeler, Brighton, date unknown.

257 *A Book of Images* by W. T. Horton and W. B. Yeats, 1898.

258 *Way of the Soul* by W. T. Horton, 1910.

259 *'The Pass' by W. T. Horton; ink drawing in the University of Reading collection.*

260 *'The Whirlwind' by W. T. Horton; ink drawing in the University of Reading collection.*

261 *'The Descent of the Vortex of Fire (The Divine Breath) to the Earth' by W. T. Horton; ink drawing in the University of Reading collection.*

262 *'The Dispersal' by W. T. Horton; ink and water-colour drawing in the University of Reading collection.*

263 *'The Grim Phantom Fear' from 'The Fall of the House of Usher' by W. T. Horton; pencil drawing in the University of Reading collection.*

264 *'Book of Illustrated Nursery Rhymes' by W. T. Horton; in the University of Reading collection.*

265 *Two illustrations for 'Jack and Jill' by W. T. Horton; pen and ink and water-colour drawing in the University of Reading collection.*

266 *'Little Bo-peep has found her Sheep' by W. T. Horton; pen and ink drawing in the University of Reading collection.*

267 *'All Mural Structures' . . . (Walls have ears) by W. T. Horton; pen and ink drawing in the University of Reading Collection.*

268 *'A Meeting of the Board' by W. T. Horton; pen and ink drawing in the University of Reading collection.*

269 *'The Spirit of Hypocrite' by W. T. Horton; pen and ink drawing in the University of Reading collection.*

270 *'A Vision of Toadyism' by W. T. Horton; pen and ink drawing In the University of Reading collection.*

271 *'The Sea Serpent' by W. T. Horton; pen and ink drawing in the University of Reading collection.*

272 *'Vision of Spirits in a Mandorla of Cloud' by W. T. Horton; crayon drawing in the University of Reading collection.*

273 *'Lady seen in dream' by W. T. Horton, 1907; pencil and crayon drawing in the University of Reading collection.*

274 *'Spirit Vision' by W. T. Horton, 1907; crayon and gilt drawing in the University of Reading collection.*

275 *'Self-portrait, with the Spirit of a lady' by W. T. Horton, 1917; pencil drawing in the University of Reading collection.*

276 *Illustrations to Thornton's Virgil by William Blake; mount of seventeen wood engravings in the Victoria and Albert Museum.*

277 *The Enchanted Castle by Claude Lorraine; oil painting in the collection of Christopher Lloyd, Esq. Photograph from owner.*

278 *'Lake Albano' by Richard Wilson; oil painting in the Lady Lever Art Gallery, Port Sunlight.*

279 *'Samuel Palmer: A Memoir' by A. H. Palmer, 1882. In the University of Reading collection.*

280 *'Life and Letters of Samuel Palmer' by A. H. Palmer, 1892; in the University of Reading collection.*

281 *'The Shorter Poems of John Milton' illustrated by Samuel Palmer, 1889; copy in the Whitworth Art Gallery, University of Manchester.*

282 *'An English Version of the Eclogues of Virgil' by Samuel Palmer, with illustration by the author, 1883; copy of second edition, 1884, in the Whitworth Art Gallery, University of Manchester.*

283 *'The Lonely Tower' by Samuel Palmer; etching in the Victoria and Albert Museum.*

284 *'The Herdsman' by Samuel Palmer; etching in the Victoria and Albert Museum.*

285 *'The Travellers' by Samuel Palmer; watercolour drawing in the Whitworth Art Gallery, University of Manchester.*

286 *'The Ploughman' by Edward Calvert; wood-engraving in the Whitworth Art Gallery, University of Manchester.*

287 *'The Brook' by Edward Calvert; wood-engraving in the Whitworth Art Gallery, University of Manchester.*

288 *'The Sheep of his Pasture' by Edward Calvert; wood-engraving in the Whitworth Art Gallery, University of Manchester.*

289 *'A Memoir of Edward Calvert' by Samuel Calvert, 1893; copy in the University of Reading collection.*

290 *'The Sleeping Shepherd' by Samuel Palmer; pen and sepia wash drawing in the Whitworth Art Gallery, University of Manchester.*

291 *Orpheus* **by Robert Gregory, c1901; oil painting in the collection of Mrs M. Kennedy.** (Pl. 30).

292 *Coole Lake* **by Robert Gregory, before 1914; oil painting in the collection of Mrs M. Kennedy.** (Pl. 29).

293 *Coole Lake* **by Robert Gregory, before 1914; oil painting in the Municipal Art Gallery, Dublin.** (Pl. 31).

294 *The Waterfall* by J. D. Innes, 1910; water-colour in the Tate Gallery. (Pl. 32).

295 *The Mountain Pool* by J. D. Innes, 1911; oil painting in the collection of The Hon. Lady Ridley. Photograph from Courtauld Institute of Art.

296 *'Seaton Mountains' by J. D. Innes, 1912; water-colour drawing in the Whitworth Art Gallery, University of Manchester.*

297 *The Van Pool* by J. D. Innes, 1912; oil painting in the collection of Hugo Pitman, Esq. Photograph from Courtauld Institute of Art.

298 *By the Lake, Arenig* by J. D. Innes, c1913; oil painting in the collection of The Earl of Sandwich. Photograph from Courtauld Institute of Art.

230   *The Court of Death*
       by G. F. Watts
       Courtesy of Norwich Museums

Plate 26

203 *Symbolic Figure*
     by J. T. Nettleship, c.1870
     University of Reading collection.

Plate 27

205 *Symbolic Figures*
    by J. T. Nettleship, c1870
    University of Reading collection

Plate 28

292　*Coole Lake*
by Robert Gregory
Mrs. M. Kennedy collection

Plate 29

291 *Orpheus*
by Robert Gregory
Mrs. M. Kennedy collection

Plate 30

293 *Coole Lake*
     by Robert Gregory
     Courtesy of the Municipal Gallery, Dublin

Plate 31

294 *The Waterfall*
by J. D. Innes
Courtesy of the Tate Gallery

Plate 32

THE DANCER

'Nothing is stated, there is no intrusion for the irrelevant purpose of describing; a world rises before one, the picture lasts only long enough to have been there; and the dancer, with her gesture, all pure symbol, evokes from her mere beautiful motion, idea, sensation, all that one need ever know of event. There, before you, she exists, in harmonious life; and her rhythm reveals to you the soul of her imagined being.'

Arthur Symons, ' *The World as Ballet.*'

Yeats was long preoccupied with the notion of 'unity' in art – the inseparability of the body of a poem and its intellectual content. He used the analogy of the beauty of women, which should also be non-intellectual, inexpressive and mysterious. He believed:

' That blest souls are not composite,
And that all beautiful women may
Live in uncomposite blessedness,
And lead us to the like – if they
Will banish every thought, unless
The lineaments that please their view
When the long looking glass is full,
Even to the footsole think it too.

('Michael Robartes and the Dancer')

He recurs frequently to this analogy, which derives from such works as Rossetti's *Lilith* ('subtly of herself contemplative') (299) and from Leonardo's *Mona Lisa* (300) and Pater's famous description of it. It lies behind Yeats's admiration for archaic and Byzantine figures. It is entirely characteristic of Yeats that he converts the 'Decadent' theme of the Fatal Woman to his own finer purposes, as he did the theme of Byzantium.

The quality of resisting the dissociation into dead elements of intellect and body Yeats found also in the art and in the aristocracy of the Italian Renaissance, and it is by this criterion that he judges the modern world. Thus he writes of two typical portraits:

' In the Dublin National Gallery there hung, perhaps still hang, upon the same wall, a portrait of some Venetian gentleman by Strozzi (301) and Mr Sargent's painting of President Wilson (302). Whatever thought broods in the dark eyes of that Venetian gentleman has drawn its life from his whole body; it feeds upon it as the flame feeds upon the candle – and should that thought be changed, his pose would change, his very cloak would rustle, for his whole body thinks[1]. President Wilson lives only in the eyes, which are steady and intent; the flesh about the mouth is dead, and the hands are dead, and the clothes suggest no movement of his body, nor any movement but that of the valet, who has brushed and folded in mechanical routine. There all was an energy flowing outward from the nature itself; here all is the anxious study and slight deflection of external force.'

('The Tragic Generation')

These ideas, so central to Yeats's thinking about art, frequently brought to his mind another Decadent theme, that of Salome. The poets and dancers of the late nineteenth century dwelt upon this image; Salome was the subject of poems by Mallarmé and Symons, as well as many lesser poets. Sometimes these are analogous to visual representations – Mallarmé's to Moreau's (303), Evan John's to Karl Burger's (304). Salome was a heroine of the Decadence; Beardsley's illustrations to Wilde's *Salome* (305) set the tone, and there is ample evidence of the degree to which she appealed to artists in search of a fantastic 'Decadence' (306, 307). But Yeats transformed her entirely, and gave her a place in his aesthetic and historical systems. As a dancer she represented the idea of the Image as non-discursive, without separable intellectual content; as the woman who demanded the head of a saint, she emblematized the cost of the artist's achievement. She haunts the work of Yeats down to the late plays.

Dancers, not only historical but actual, were important to Yeats. In the nineties he moved in circles where music-hall dancers could be admired as 'Maenads of the Decadence' (Symons) and where their art was regarded as exemplary to poetry (this view, found in Mallarmé and in Symons, persists in Valéry and Mr Eliot; and it survives, philosophically chastened, in the works of Mrs Langer). 'The avoidance of emphasis', wrote Symons, 'the evasive, winding turn of things; and, above all, the intellectual as well as sensuous appeal of a living symbol, which can but reach the brain through the eyes, in the visual, concrete, imaginative way, has seemed to make the ballet concentrate in itself a good deal of the modern ideal in matters of artistic expression'.

Symons enjoyed the ballet; but most of the admired performers were exponents of various kinds of 'free' dancing. Very important was Jane Avril, often drawn by Toulouse-Lautrec for posters (308, 309), and the dancer in Symons' best dance-poem *La Mélinite: Moulin Rouge.* Part of the interest in Jane Avril was certainly of a pathological kind; she was a patient of Charcot's. Even more applauded as representing 'the modern ideal of artistic expression' was the American dancer Loïe Fuller, whom Yeats recalls by name in *Nineteen Hundred and Nineteen.* At the Folies Bergère in the Nineties she danced in a whirl of shining draperies manipulated on sticks (310, 311, 312, 313, 314, 315, 316). She continued for many years – at first alone and later with a company – to practise a form of dancing which almost eliminated the human body and concentrated the attention of the spectators on the movement of silk under electric light. The Toulouse-Lautrec oil is presumably of the Fire Dance, which had the greatest success with the poets of the time. Yeats is probably recalling it when he speaks in *Byzantium* of the mosaics on 'the Emperor's pavement' where human souls:

> 'all complexities of fury leave,
> Dying into a dance,
> An agony of trance,
> An agony of flame that cannot singe a sleeve.'

Such dancing seemed to Mallarmé 'a spectacle defying all definition, radiant, homogeneous'. In the words of André Levinson the dancer is 'révélatrice du réel'; and when Mallarmé speaks of such dancing as 'une écriture corporelle', and as 'poème dégagé de tout appareil du scribe', he reminds us of Yeats's climactic use of the Dancer at the end of *Among Schoolchildren*:

> 'O body swayed to music, O brightening glance,
> How can we know the dancer from the dance?'

It is this surrender of personality to the objectified emotion of the dance, this immolation of intellect in body, that Yeats had in mind (among other matters) when he wrote in his 'system' poem, *The Double Vision of Michael Robartes,* of a visionary dancer who 'had outdanced thought'.[2]

Yeats's interest in dancing and the inexpressive face is reflected in his views on drama (see Section III). He hated 'character' and 'rhetoric'. The Japanese Noh drama, to which he was introduced by Ezra Pound, seemed to embody all his theories in a highly developed and suitably aristocratic form, and he proceeded to write his own dance-plays, which avoid all naturalistic movement and speech, and all facial expression. The mask made for Yeats by Dulac may be compared with an authentic Noh mask (317).

Frank Kermode

NOTES
1   Here Yeats is remembering those lines from Donne's *Second Anniversary* which were so often quoted to similar ends in the late nineteenth century:

> 'Her pure and eloquent blood
> Spoke in her cheekes, and so distinctly wrought,
> That one might almost say, her body thought.' (ll.244–6)

2   For a fuller account of these dancers see my *Poet and Dancer before Diaghilev,* Partisan Review, Jan./Feb. 1961, pp48–76, and *Romantic Image* (Routledge & Kegan Paul, 1957).

299 *Lady Lilith* by D. G. Rossetti; oil painting in the Metropolitan Museum, New York.

300 *Mona Lisa* by Leonardo da Vinci; oil painting in the Musée du Louvre, Paris.

301 *Portrait of a Gentleman* by Bernardo Strozzi; oil painting in the National Gallery of Ireland, Dublin. (Pl. 33).

302 *Portrait of President Woodrow Wilson* by J. S. Sargent; oil painting in the National Gallery of Ireland, Dublin. (Pl. 34).

303 *L'Apparition* by Gustave Moreau; oil painting in the Musée du Louvre, Paris.

304 *Salome with Head of John the Baptist;* statue by Karl Burger. Photograph from Däffner's *Salome*, Munich, 1912.

305 *Two illustrations to Oscar Wilde's Salome, 1894 by Aubrey Beardsley; autotype facsimiles in the University of Reading collection.*

306 *Salome with Head of John the Baptist*, oil painting by Lovis Corinth. Photograph from Däffner's *Salome*, Munich, 1912.

307 *Salome*, oil painting by Marcel Beronneau. Photograph from Däffner's *Salome*, Munich, 1912.

308 *Jane Avril aux Serpents* poster by H. de Toulouse-Lautrec. Photograph from Courtauld Institute of Art.

309 *Jane Avril, lithograph by H. de Toulouse-Lautrec; reproduction in the University of Reading collection.*

310 *Loie Fuller in the Folies Bergéres* by H. de Toulouse-Lautrec; oil sketch in the Musée Toulouse-Lautrec, Albi. (Pl. 35).

311 *Loie Fuller outside the Louvre,* c1914. Photograph from *Picture Post* library.

312 *Skirt Dancing – Mademoiselle Loie Fuller and her Transformations.* Photograph from magazine, source unknown.

313 *Loie Fuller;* photographed by Flatters and Garnett from engraving by Steinlen.

314 *The Butterfly Dance – Miss Loie Fuller in one of her 'Mysterious Dances'* at the Palace Theatre. Reproduction from *Illustrated Budget,* 10th October 1903.

315 *Loie Fuller* by T. T. Heine, reproduced *Die Insel;* photograph from Routledge and Kegan Paul Ltd.

316 *'A Dancer' by W. T. Horton; illustration in the University of Reading collection.*

317 *Noh Mask.* Photograph from frontispiece to Arthur Waley, *The Nō Plays of Japan,* 1921.

301 *Portrait of a Gentleman*
     by B. Strozzi
     Courtesy of the National Gallery of Ireland

Plate 33

302 *President Wilson*
   by J. S. Sargent
   Courtesy of the National Gallery of Ireland

Plate 34

310 *Loie Fuller*
by H. de Touluse-Lautrec
Courtesy of Musée Toulouse-Lautrec, Albi

Plate 35

BOOKS AND MANUSCRIPTS

The collection of books, periodicals, and manuscripts displayed in this exhibition is not intended to cover the whole of Yeats's work, but rather to give an impression of the variety and extent of his labours. It is intended, also, to show something of the ways in which Yeats revised his poems and plays, and to indicate some of his, perhaps transitory, enthusiasms. Yeats was an impresario as well as a poet; he was constantly editing or introducing the work of others, and, as several critics have pointed out, he rarely allowed a book or author that interested him to escape without giving him ideas or imagery for his verse. His championship of Blake and Spenser in his early days provided him with much material, as also did his later interest in Synge, Brian Merriman, Tagore, and a host of others. Even his short preface to Oliver Gogarty's *An Offering of Swans* has some significance; as Giorgio Melchiori has suggested, he may well have had Gogarty's work in his mind while composing his own poem about Leda.

This alone would not justify the inclusion in an exhibition of this kind of so many minor works. It is, however, in the appearance of many of these books and magazines that we can find a clue to the changing tastes and attitudes of the years during which Yeats wrote his works. In some cases we know that Yeats himself either commissioned or delighted in the designs upon the covers of his books. The letters to Sturge Moore alone show the importance Yeats attached to the appearance of his work; the correspondence about the designs for *The Tower* and *The Winding Stair* is both detailed and lengthy. Other aspects of Yeats are also illuminated by a glance along the hundreds of volumes in which his words appeared. His continual searching after some society, or group, in which he could feel at home, and which was dominated by some high artistic purpose or philosophy, is not only evident in his writings, but also in the succession of anthologies, and periodicals, which he dominated. *The Book of the Rhymers' Club* gives way to *Beltaine* and *Samhain,* and these in their turn give way to the publication of series of *Broadsides,* and to the publication, for an intimate circle, in limited editions, of plays intended only for performance to a small group of initiates. Yeats was 'Movement-conscious'. It might be said, with only an allowable amount of exaggeration, that he invented the Irish Literary Revival. Certainly, his belief in the necessity of a few people of ideals getting together and producing things of beauty and significance in order ultimately to alter and reform the society in which they live, is clearly shown by his work for the Cuala Press, a firm formed resolutely in the Morris tradition. His continual and perhaps rather Pre-Raphaelite desire to unify the arts of painting and poetry is also illustrated by the broadsheets he edited, and by the illustrations to, and the designs of, many of his books.

The final impression is, however, of restless industry. The sheer bulk of work is itself impressive. And the continual re-ordering and revising of that work can only be appreciated, perhaps, if one sees the solid objects, the books themselves, laid out together. Gathering so many books together is a difficult matter. This exhibition could not have existed without the generosity of Trinity College, Dublin, the University of Reading, and the Brotherton Library of Leeds University. They have lent books freely, and helped also in many other ways. Nor could the exhibition have been staged without the assistance of the late Alan Wade's superb *Bibliography*. This book has made it unnecessary to describe each item shown in detail. I have simply given short titles, and referred the reader to the entry in Wade for further information. A copy of Wade is available for consultation in the Exhibition. I have been sparing of notes upon the exhibits, preferring that they should speak for themselves, and I have chosen to display more content-matter than title-pages in order that Yeats's own words may provide some kind of commentary.

In the catalogue itself I have indicated the source of the exhibits by letters, T C D for Trinity College Dublin, U of R for the University of Reading, B L for the Brotherton Library Leeds, and R S for myself. The catalogue is arranged chronologically, although, for purposes of comparing different texts, the exhibits themselves are not always set out in this way. It seemed important both to provide a chronological order, and to enable quick comparisons to be made between books of different periods.

Robin Skelton

(Notes on Abbreviations—T C D: Trinity College, Dublin; U of R: University of Reading; B L: Brotherton Library, Leeds; and R S: Robin Skelton).

1 **The Dublin University Review** 1885
U of R

Contains: *The Seeker, A Dramatic Poem in Two Scenes* and an Epilogue to *The Island of Statues* and *The Seeker.*

2 **The Irish Monthly** 1887
U of R

3 **Fairy and Folk Tales of the Irish Peasantry**
Edited and Selected by W. B. Yeats
Walter Scott, London
Thomas Whittaker, New York
W. J. Gage and Co, Toronto 1888
Wade No. 212 U of R

4 **The Wanderings of Oisin** and Other Poems
By W. B. Yeats
Kegan Paul, Trench & Co 1889
Wade No. 2 T C D
500 copies were printed.

5 **Representative Irish Tales**
Compiled, with an Introduction and Notes by W. B. Yeats
G. P. Putman and Sons, New York and London March 1891
Wade No. 215 U of R

6 **Ganconagh: John Sherman and Dhoya**
T. Fisher Unwin November 1891
Wade No. 4 R S

This is number 10 of the Pseudonym Library. The Author's identity was not intended to be much of a secret, however, for Yeats had already published the poem which appears on page 187 in *The Wanderings of Oisin* under his own name.

Together with an initialled review from the *Illustrated London News* of 21st November 1891.

7 **Irish Fairy Tales**
Edited with an Introduction by W. B. Yeats
T. Fisher Unwin   1892
Wade No. 216   R S

8 **The Countess Kathleen** and Various Legends and Lyrics
By W. B. Yeats
T. Fisher Unwin   September 1892
Wade No. 6   T C D
530 copies were printed.

9 **The Works of William Blake**: Poetic, Symbolic and Critical
Edited with Lithographs of the Illustrated 'Prophetic Books', and
a Memoir and Interpretation by Edwin John Ellis . . . and William
Butler Yeats
Quaritch   1893
Wade No. 218   U of R
500 copies were printed.

10 **The Poems of William Blake**
Edited by W. B. Yeats
Lawrence and Bullen   1893
Charles Scribner's Sons, New York
Wade No. 219   R S

11 **Irish Fairy and Folk Tales**
Selected and Edited with Introduction by W. B. Yeats
Walter Scott, Ltd   October 1893
Wade No. 223   U of R

12 **The Celtic Twilight**: Men and Women, Dhouls and Faeries
By W. B. Yeats
Lawrence and Bullen   December 1893
Wade No. 8   U of R

13 **The Land of Heart's Desire**
By W. B. Yeats
T. Fisher Unwin   1894
Wade No. 10   T C D

14 **A Book of Irish Verse**
Selected from Modern Writers with an Introduction and Notes
by W. B. Yeats
Methuen and Co   March 1895
Wade No. 225   U of R

15 **Poems**
By W. B. Yeats
T. Fisher Unwin   October 1895
Wade No. 15   U of R
775 copies were printed, of which 25 were on vellum and signed
by the Author.

16 The Savoy

January, April, July, August 1896

R S

The Binding of the Hair was reprinted in *The Secret Rose* 1897 but omitted from the *Collected Works* of 1908 and all later collections.

17 The Pageant
Edited by C. Hazelwood Shannon
and J. W. Gleeson White
Henry and Co   1896
Wade No. 295   R S
Yeats contributed the story *Costello the Proud, Oona Macdermott, and the Bitter Tongue*, which was reprinted in *The Secret Rose* 1897.

17a The Secret Rose
By W. B. Yeats
Lawrence and Bullen Ltd   April 1897
Wade No. 21   U of R

18 The Dome: A quarterly containing examples of all the arts.
The Unicorn Press   May 1897

R S

This contains *The Desire of Man and of Woman* which was reprinted with the title *Mongan Laments the Change that has come upon him and his Beloved* in *The Wind Among the Reeds*, 1899.

19 The Tables of the Law: The Adoration of the Magi
By W. B. Yeats
Privately Printed   June 1897
Wade No. 24   U of R
110 copies were printed.

20 The Yellow Book   April 1897
Wade No. 322   U of R
Contains: *The Blessed.*

21 A Book of Images
Drawn by W. T. Horton and Introduced by W. B. Yeats
Unicorn Press   1898
Wade No. 255   R S

22 The Nineteenth Century   January 1898

U of R

Contains: *The Prisoners of the Gods.*

23 Cosmopolis   June 1898

U of R

Contains: *The Celtic Element in Literature.*

24 The Fortnightly Review   1898

U of R

Contains: *The Broken Gates of Death.*

25 **The Winds among the Reeds**
By W. B. Yeats
Shakespeare Head Press April 1899
Wade No. 27 T C D
The cover design is by Althea Gyles.

26 **Poems**
By W. B. Yeats
T. Fisher Unwin 1899
Wade No. 17 R S
The Second English Edition, revised.
The cover design is by Althea Gyles.

27 **Literary Ideals in Ireland**
By John Eglinton; W. B. Yeats, A E; W. Larminie
T. Fisher Unwin May 1899
Wade No. 297 T C D

28 **Beltaine**
Edited by W. B. Yeats
The Organ of the Irish Literary Theatre 1899–1900
Wade No. 226 T C D and U of R
Three numbers were issued in May 1899, February 1900, and
April 1900. They were afterwards bound up together and issued
as one volume.

29 **The Shadowy Waters**
By W. B. Yeats
Hodder and Stoughton 1900
Wade No. 30 R S

30 **Is the Order of R.R. & A.C. to remain a Magical Order?**
March 1901
Wade No. 33 T C D
Wade states: 'The Order Rubidae Rosae & Aureae Crucis was
apparently a section of the Order of the Golden Dawn, the
Mystical Society to which Yeats belonged'.

31 **Cuchulain of Muirthemne:** The story of the Men of the
Red Branch of Ulster
Arranged and put into English by Lady Gregory, with a Preface
by W. B. Yeats
John Murray 1902
Wade No. 256 R S

32 **The Celtic Twilight**
By W. B. Yeats
A. H. Bullen 1902
Wade No. 35 R S
A revised and enlarged edition.

33 Cathleen ni Houlihan: A play in One Act and in Prose
By W. B. Yeats
A. H. Bullen   1902
Wade No. 40   T C D

34 Samhain: An occasional review
Edited by W. B. Yeats
T. Fisher Unwin   October 1902
Wade No. 228   U of R
This contains *Cathleen ni Houlihan.*

35 Where There Is Nothing: Being Volume One of plays for
an Irish Theatre
By W. B. Yeats
A. H. Bullen   1903
Wade No. 44   R S

36 Ideas of Good and Evil
By W. B. Yeats
A. H. Bullen   1903
Wade No. 46   T C D

37 In The Seven Woods
By W. B. Yeats
Dun Emer Press   1903
Wade No. 49   T C D
325 copies were printed.

38 The Hour-Glass: A Morality
By W. B. Yeats
Wm. Heinemann   1903
Wade No. 51   T C D
Twelve copies only were printed.

39 Samhain: An occasional review
Edited by W. B. Yeats
Sealy Bryers & Walker and T. Fisher Unwin   September 1903
Wade No. 229   U of R

40 The Tables of the Law and the Adoration of the Magi
Elkin Matthews   1904
Wade No. 25   R S
The first published edition.

41 The Hour Glass, Cathleen ni Houlihan, The Pot of Broth:
Being Volume Two of plays for an Irish Theatre
By W. B. Yeats
A. H. Bullen   1904
Wade No. 53   U of R

42 The King's Threshold: and On Baile's Strand: Being
Volume Three of plays for an Irish Theatre
By W. B. Yeats
A. H. Bullen 1904
Wade No. 56 R S

43 Stories of Red Hanrahan
By William Butler Yeats
The Dun Emer Press 1904
Wade No. 59 T C D
500 copies were printed.

44 Samhain: an occasional review
Edited by W. B. Yeats
T. Fisher Unwin December 1904
Wade No. 230 R S

45 Gods and Fighting Men: The story of the Tuatha de Danaan
and of the Fianna of Ireland
Arranged and put into English by Lady Gregory, with a Preface
by W. B. Yeats
John Murray 1904
Wade No. 258 R S

46 The Love Songs of Connacht: Being the Fourth Chapter
of the Songs of Connacht
Collected and Translated by Douglas Hyde, LL.D., 'An Craobhin
Aiobhinn' President of the Gaelic League
Dun Emer Press 1904
Wade No. 260 T C D
The Preface is by W. B. Yeats.

47 The Poets' Corner
By Max Beerbohm
Heinemann 1904
R S
This contains the first printing of 'Mr W. B. Yeats, presenting
Mr George Moore to the Queen of the Fairies'.

48 The Hour-Glass, Cathleen ni Houlihan, The Pot of Broth
By W. B. Yeats
Maunsel & Co Ltd, Dublin 1905
Wade No. 54 R S

49 On Baile's Strand
By W. B. Yeats
Maunsel & Co Ltd, Dublin 1905
Wade No. 58 T C D

50 Letter to Edmund Gosse, 20th November 1905
Unpublished B L

51 **Letter to Edward Clodd,** 6th November
   Unpublished   B L
52 **The Well of the Saints:** Being Volume Four of plays for an
   Irish Theatre
   By J. M. Synge, with an Introduction by W. B. Yeats
   A. H. Bullen   1905
   Wade No. 262   R S
53 **Poems of Spenser:** Selected and with an Introduction by
   W. B. Yeats
   The Caxton Publishing Co   1906
   Wade No. 235   R S
   This is the second issue of the book. The first was published by
   T. C. & E. C. Jack of Edinburgh, who sold sets of the sheets to
   The Caxton Publishing Co.
54 **The Shanachie:** An Illustrated Irish Miscellany
   Maunsel & Co Ltd, Dublin   Vol. I, 1906
                                                                  R S

55 **The Hour-Glass:** A Morality
   By W. B. Yeats
   A. H. Bullen   1907
   Wade No. 67   R S
   Theatre edition.
56 **Deidre:** Being Volume Five of plays for an Irish Theater
   By W. B. Yeats
   Maunsel & Co Ltd, Dublin   1907
   Wade No. 69   R S
57 **The Shanachie:** An Illustrated Irish Miscellany
   Maunsel·& Co Ltd, Dublin   Vol. II, 1907
                                                                  R S

58 **Discoveries;** A Volume of Essays
   By William Butler Yeats
   Dun Emer Press   1907
   Wade No. 72   T C D
   200 copies were printed.
58a **The Arrow**
   Edited by W. B. Yeats   June 1907
   Wade No. 236   R S
   Contains an untitled note about Yeats which was later called
   On Taking the Playboy to London.
59 **Poems**
   By W. B. Yeats
   T. Fisher Unwin   1908
   Wade No. 20   R S
   The fifth edition.

60 The Collected Works in Verse and Prose of William Butler Yeats
The Shakespeare Head Press   Vols. 1–8, 1908
Wade Nos. 75–82   R S, U of R

61 The Nation   1908
Wade No. 341   U of R
Contains: *A Dream*. The note in prose which accompanies it has never been *reprinted.*

62 Samhain: An occasional review
Edited by W. B. Yeats
Maunsel and T. Fisher Unwin   November 1908
Wade No. 241   U of R

63 Cathleen ni Houlihan
By W. B. Yeats
A. H. Bullen   1909
Wade No. 63   R S
The second theatre edition.

64 William Butler Yeats. Poems: Second Series
A. H. Bullen   1909
Wade No. 83   R S

65 Poems and Translations
By John M. Synge
Cuala Press   1909
Wade No. 243   R S
Yeats contributed a long essay on Synge.
250 copies were printed.

66 Poems and Translations
By John M. Synge
Printed for John Quinn, New York   1909
Wade No. 244   R S
Fifty copies were printed, five of them on vellum.

67 The Green Helmet and Other Poems
By William Butler Yeats
The Cuala Press   1910
Wade No. 84   U of R
400 copies were printed.

68 Deirdre of the Sorrows: A play
By John M. Synge
Cuala Press   1910
Wade No. 245   R S
The text of this play was assembled from Synge's many drafts after his death by W. B. Yeats, Lady Gregory and Molly Allgood. 250 copies were printed.
There is a Preface by Yeats.

69 **Deirdre of the Sorrows:** A play
By John M. Synge
Printed for John Quinn, New York 1910
Wade No. 246 R S
John Quinn printed 50 copies of this book, five of which were on vellum. On discovering that the text as printed differed from that of a manuscript version in his possession he decided to destroy all but 10 copies of this edition, and publish a new version. In fact, it seems this was not done, but in an unknown number of copies Quinn inserted twelve un-numbered pages, nine of them having corrections to the text. This copy is one of the original edition without these extra pages.

70 **Deidre**
By William Butler Yeats
Shakespeare Head Press 1911
Wade No. 86 R S
The first theatre edition.

71 **Synge and the Ireland of His Time**
By William Butler Yeats
With a note concerning a walk through Connemara with him by Jack Butler Yeats
The Cuala Press 1911
Wade No. 88 R S
350 copies were printed.

72 **The Green Helmet:** An heroic farce
By W. B. Yeats
Shakespeare Head Press 1911
Wade No. 89 R S
Theatre edition. The only separate edition of the play.

73 **Plays for an Irish Theatre**
By W. B. Yeats, with Designs by Gordon Craig.
A. H. Bullen 1911
Wade No. 92 R S

74 **The Countess Cathleen**
By W. B. Yeats
T. Fisher Unwin 1912
Wade No. 93 T C D
The revised version.

75 **Poems Written in Discouragement**
By W. B. Yeats, 1912—1913
Cuala Press 1913
Wade No. 107 T C D
50 copies were printed.

76 **Gitanjali** (Song Offerings)
By Rabindranath Tagore
A collection of Prose Translations made by the Author from
the original Bengali with an Introduction by W. B. Yeats
Macmillan & Co, Limited   1913
Wade No. 264   R S
The Second Edition. The First Edition was one of 750 copies
printed for The India Society in 1912.

77 **Our Irish Theatre:** A Chapter of Autobiography
By Lady Gregory
G. P. Putnam's Sons, New York and London   1913
Wade No. 307   U of R
This includes Yeats's *Advice to Playwrights who are sending
Plays to the Abbey, Dublin.*

78 **The Hour Glass**
By W. B. Yeats
Cuala Press   1914
Wade No. 108   T C D
This is a new version of the play. 50 copies were printed.

79 **Responsibilities:** Poems and a Play
By William Butler Yeats
The Cuala Press   1914
Wade No. 110   U of R
400 copies were printed.

80 **Reveries over Childhood and Youth**
By William Butler Yeats
The Cuala Press   1915
Wade No. 111   T C D
425 copies were printed.

81 **Three Letters to Gosse,** July 1915

                                                                B L
These letters were written in order to get financial help for
James Joyce from the Royal Literary Fund.

82 **Form:** A quarterly of the Arts
Edited by Austin O. Spare and Francis Marsden
John Lane   No. 1, Vol. I, 1916
                                                                R S

83 **Eight Poems**
By W. B. Yeats.
Transcribed by Edward Pay
Published by *Form* at the Morland Press Ltd   1916
Wade No. 114   R S
200 copies were printed.

84 **Easter, 1916**
By W. B. Yeats
Privately Printed by Clement Shorter   1916
Wade No. 117   T C D
Twenty five copies were printed for private circulation.

85 **Reveries over Childhood and Youth**
By William Butler Yeats
Macmillan and Co, Limited   1916
Wade No. 113   R S
The first English Edition.

86 **Certain Noble Plays of Japan:** From the manuscripts of
Ernest Fenollosa
Chosen and finished by Ezra Pound, with an Introduction by
William Butler Yeats.
Cuala Press   1916
Wade No. 269   T C D
350 copies were printed.

87 **The Wild Swans at Coole:** other Verses and a Play in Verse
By W. B. Yeats
The Cuala Press   1917
Wade No. 118   R S
400 copies were printed.

88 **Two Manuscript Poems**
        R S
These poems first appeared in *The Wild Swans at Coole,* but the
manuscripts differ from both early and late texts, making it likely
that they were written out about 1920.

89 **Per Amica Silentia Lunae**
By William Butler Yeats
Macmillan and Co, Ltd   1918
Wade No. 120   U of R

90 **Two Plays for Dancers**
By W. B. Yeats
The Cuala Press   1919
Wade No. 123   U of R
400 copies were printed.

91 **The Cutting of an Agate**
By W. B. Yeats
Macmillan and Co, Limited   1919
Wade No. 126   R S
The first English Edition. The first American Edition appeared in
1912.

92 **The Dial**   November 1920
   Wade No. 350   U of R
   Contains: *Michael Robartes and the Dancer, Under Saturn, Sixteen Dead Men, Demon and Beast, A Meditation in Time of War, Towards Break of Day, On a Political Prisoner, The Second Coming, An Image from a Past Life, The Rose Tree, Easter 1916.*

93 **Michael Robartes and the Dancer**
   By William Butler Yeats
   The Cuala Press   1920
   Wade No. 127   U of R
   400 copies were printed.

94 **Visions and Beliefs in the West of Ireland**
   Collected and Arranged by Lady Gregory, with two Essays and Notes by W. B. Yeats
   G. P. Putnam's Sons, New York and London   1920
   Wade No. 312   U of R

95 **Four Plays for Dancers**
   By W. B. Yeats
   Macmillan and Co, Limited   1921
   Wade No. 129   R S

96 **Four Years**
   By William Butler Yeats
   The Cuala Press   1921
   Wade No. 131   U of R
   400 copies were printed.

97 **Hugh Lane's Life and Achievement:** with some account of the Dublin Galleries
   By Lady Gregory
   John Murray   1921
   Wade No. 313   R S

98 **Seven Poems and a Fragment**
   By William Butler Yeats
   The Cuala Press   1922
   Wade No. 132   T C D
   500 copies were printed.

99 **The Trembling of the Veil**
   By W. B. Yeats
   T. Werner Laurie   1922
   Wade No. 133   U of R
   1000 copies were printed, each signed by the author.

100 Together with a prospectus and a copy of the reader's report. This latter was probably circulated to chosen booksellers or likely subscribers.

                                                                R S

101 **Later Poems**
By W. B. Yeats
Macmillan and Co, Ltd   1922
Wade No. 134   R S

102 **Plays in Prose and Verse:** Written for an Irish Theatre and
generally with the help of a friend
By W. B. Yeats
Macmillan and Co, Ltd   1922
Wade No. 136   U of R

103 **The Player Queen**
By W. B. Yeats
Macmillan and Co, Ltd   1922
Wade No. 138   T C D

104 **Plays and Controversies**
By W. B. Yeats
Macmillan and Co, Ltd   1923
Wade No. 139   U of R

105 **Early Memories:** Some Chapers of Autobiography
By John Butler Yeats
The Cuala Press   1923
Wade No. 272   U of R
500 copies were printed. W. B. Yeats contributed a Preface.

106 **Essays**
By W. B. Yeats
Macmillan and Co, Ltd   1924
Wade No. 141   U of R

107 **The Cat and the Moon:** and certain poems
By William Butler Yeats
The Cuala Press   1924
Wade No. 145   R S
500 copies were printed.

108 **An Offering of Swans**
By Oliver Gogarty
The Cuala Press   1923
Wade No. 273   R S
There is a Preface by W. B. Yeats. 300 copies were printed.

109 **The Bounty of Sweden:** A meditation, and a lecture delivered
before the Royal Swedish Academy, and certain Notes by
William Butler Yeats
The Cuala Press   1924
Wade No. 146   T C D
400 copies were printed.

110 **Early Poems and Stories**
By W. B. Yeats
Macmillan and Co, Ltd   1925
Wade No. 147   U of R

111 **A Vision:** An explanation of life founded upon the writing of Giraldus and upon certain doctrines attributed to Kusta Ben Luka
By William Butler Yeats
T. Werner Laurie   1925
Wade No. 149   T C D
600 copies were printed, each signed by the author.

112 Together with a prospectus and three reviews of the book. R S

113 **Axel**
By Jean Marie Matthias Phillippe Auguste, Count de Villiers de L'Isle-Adam
Translated into English by H. P. R. Finberg, with a Preface by Willian Butler Yeats
Jarrolds   1925
Wade No. 275   T C D
500 copies were printed

114 Together with a prospectus and two reviews of the book.   R S

115 **Estrangement:** Being some Fifty Thoughts from a Diary kept by William Butler Yeats in the year Nineteen hundred and nine
The Cuala Press   1926
Wade No. 150   T C D
300 copies were printed.

116 **The London Mercury**   1926
    U of R

Contains *Estrangement: Thoughts from a Diary kept in 1909.*

117 **Autobiographies:** Reveries over Childhood and Youth and the Trembling of the Veil
By W. B. Yeats
Macmillan and Co, Ltd   1926
Wade No. 151   U of R

118 **The Midnight Court:** and the Adventures of a Luckless Fellow
Translated from the Gaelic by Percy Arland Ussher, with a Preface by W. B. Yeats, and Woodcuts by Frank W. Peers
Jonathan Cape   1926
Wade No. 276   R S

119 **Poems**
By W. B. Yeats
T. Fisher Unwin Ltd (Ernest Benn Ltd)   1927
Wade No. 153   R S
A new, fully revised, edition.

120 **October Blast**
By William Butler Yeats
The Cuala Press 1927
Wade No. 156 T C D
350 copies were printed.

121 **Stories of Red Hanrahan and The Secret Rose**
By W. B. Yeats
Illustrated and Decorated by Norah McGuiness
Macmillan and Co, Ltd 1927
Wade No. 157 R S
A copy in the variant red cloth binding mentioned by Wade.

122 **The Tower**
By W. B. Yeats
Macmillan and Co, Ltd 1928
Wade No. 158 R S
The gold design on the cover is by T. Sturge Moore.

123 **Sophocles' King Oedipus:** A version for the modern stage
By W. B. Yeats
Macmillan and Co, Ltd 1928
Wade No. 160 U of R

124 **The Death of Synge:** and other passages from an old diary
By William Butler Yeats
The Cuala Press 1928
Wade No. 162 R S
400 copies were printed.

125 **A Packet for Ezra Pound**
By William Butler Yeats
The Cuala Press 1929
Wade No. 163 T C D
425 copies were printed.

126 **Three Things**
By W. B. Yeats
Drawings by Gilbert Spencer
Faber & Faber 1929
Wade No. 166 R S

127 **Stories of Michael Robartes and His Friends:** An extract
from a record made by his pupils: and a play in prose
By W. B. Yeats
The Cuala Press 1931
Wade No. 167 U of R
450 copies were printed.

128 **Coole**
By Lady Gregory
The Cuala Press 1931
Wade No. 319 U of R
250 copies printed.
Yeats contributed the poem, *Coole Park.* 250 copies printed.

129 **Words for Music Perhaps:** and Other Poems
By W. B. Yeats
The Cuala Press 1932
Wade No. 168 T C D
450 copies were printed.

130 **The Winding Stair:** and Other Poems
By W. B. Yeats
Macmillan and Co, Ltd 1933
Wade No. 169 R S
The design stamped on the cover is by T. Sturge Moore.

131 **Letters to the New Island**
By William Butler Yeats
Edited with an Introduction by Horace Reynolds
Oxford University Press
Harvard University Press 1934
Wade No. 173 T C D

132 **The Words upon the Window Pane:** A Play in One Act
with Notes upon the play and its subject, by William Butler Yeats
The Cuala Press 1934
Wade No. 174 T C D
350 copies were printed.

133 **Wheels and Butterflies**
By W. B. Yeats
Macmillan and Co, Ltd 1934
Wade No. 175 U of R

134 **The Collected Plays** of W. B. Yeats
Macmillan and Co, Ltd 1934
Wade No. 177 T C D

135 **The King of the Great Clock Tower:** Commentaries and
Poems by William Butler Yeats
The Cuala Press 1934
Wade No. 179 T C D
400 copies were printed.

136 **A Full Moon in March**
By W. B. Yeats
Macmillan and Co, Ltd 1935
Wade No. 182 R S

137 **Dramatis Personae**
By William Butler Yeats
The Cuala Press   1935
Wade No. 183   T C D
400 copies were printed.

138 **Broadsides:** A collection of Old and New Songs, 1935
Songs by W. B. Yeats, James Stephens, F. R. Higgins, Frank
O'Connor, Lynn Doyle, Bryan Guiness, Padraic Colum.
Illustrations by Jack B. Yeats, Victor Brown, Sean O'Sullivan,
E. C. Peet, Harry Kernoff, Maurice McGonigal.
Music by Arthur Duff.
The Cuala Press   1935
Wade No. 249   T C D
The Broadsides were edited by W. B. Yeats and F. R. Higgins
and were published monthly throughout 1935. Each broadside
was printed in an edition of 300 copies. The bound edition was
limited to 100 copies. This copy also contains the 1937 Broad-
sides which contained:
Songs by W. B. Yeats, W. J. Turner, Oliver Gogarty, Hilaire
Belloc, Dorothy Wellesley, James Stephens, Edith Sitwell,
Frank O'Connor, Gordon Bottomley, F. R. Higgins, Padraic
Colum, Walter de la Mare.
Illustrations by Jack B. Yeats, Victor Brown, Harry Kernoff,
Maurice McGonigal.
Music by W. J. Turner, Arthur Duff, Edmund Dulac, Frank
Liebich, Hilda Matheson, Art O'Murnaghan, Hilaire Belloc.

139 **Modern Poetry**
By W. B. Yeats
The Eighteenth of the Broadcast National Lectures delivered on
11th October 1936
The British Broadcasting Company   1936
Wade No. 188   T C D

140 **The Ten Principal Upanishads**
Put into English by Shree Purohit Swami and W. B. Yeats
Faber and Faber Limited   1937
Wade No. 252   T C D

141 **The Lemon Tree**
By Margot Ruddock, with an Introduction by W. B. Yeats
J. M. Dent & Sons Ltd   1937
Wade No. 284   R S

142 **The Herne's Egg:** A stage play
By W. B. Yeats
Macmillan and Co, Ltd   1938
Wade No. 195   T C D

143 **New Poems**
By W. B. Yeats
The Cuala Press   1938
Wade No. 197   T C D
450 copies were printed.

144 **The London Mercury**   1938
                                                   U of R
Contains: *The Great Day, Parnell, What was Lost, To a Friend, The Old Stone Cross, Those Images, Lapis Lazuli, The Wild Old Wicked Man, An Acre of Grass, Are You Content?, Sweet Dancer, Hound Voice, High Talk, John Kinsella's Lament for Mrs. Mary Moore, The Apparitions, A Nativity.*

145 **Last Poems and Two Plays**
By William Butler Yeats
The Cuala Press   1939
Wade No. 200   T C D
500 copies were printed.

146 **On The Boiler**
By W. B. Yeats
The Cuala Press   1939
Wade No. 202   R S
The second edition. All but four copies of the first edition were destroyed.

147 **The Arrow:** W. B. Yeats Commemoration Number
Edited by Lennox Robinson   Summer 1939
Wade No. 236   T C D
The Arrow, edited by W. B. Yeats, appeared five times—in October 1906, November 1906, February 1907, June 1907, and August 1909. The title was revived for this tribute issued by the Abbey Theatre.

148 **If I Were Four-and-Twenty**
By William Butler Yeats
The Cuala Press   1940
Wade No. 205   R S
450 copies were printed.

149 **Letters on Poetry**
From W. B. Yeats to Dorothy Wellesley
Oxford University Press   1940
Wade No. 325   U of R

150 **Mosada**
By W. B. Yeats
Cuala Press   1943
Wade No. 206   T C D
50 copies were printed. The text follows that of 1889, but incorporates the corrections Yeats made in his own copy.

151 **Pages from a Diary:** Written in Nineteen hundred and thirty
By William Butler Yeats
The Cuala Press   1944
Wade No. 207   U of R
280 copies were printed.

152 **J. B. Yeats:** Letters to his son W. B. Yeats and Others, 1869-1922
Edited with a memoir by Joseph Hone and a Preface by Oliver Elton
Faber and Faber Limited   1944
Wade No. 332   R S
This contains many letters by W. B. Yeats.

153 **Florence Farr, Bernard Shaw, W. B. Yeats. Letters**
Edited by Clifford Bax
Home & Van Thal Ltd   1946
Wade No. 329   R S
This collection was first published by the Cuala Press in 1941, and published in the U.S.A. the following year. The book shown is the first English Edition.

154 **Tribute to Thomas Davis**
By W. B. Yeats, with an account of the Thomas Davis Centenary Meeting held in Dublin on November 20th, 1914, including Dr Mahaffy's Prohibition of the 'Man Called Pearse', and an unpublished protest by 'A.E.'
Cork University Press
Oxford: B. H. Blackwell Ltd   1947
Wade No. 208   U of R

155 **The Poems** of W. B. Yeats, Vols. I and II
Macmillan and Co, Ltd   1949
Wade Nos. 209–210   U of R
This is the Definitive Edition of Yeats' poems. It was limited to 375 copies signed by the author.

156 **Diarmuid and Grania:** A Play in Three Acts
By George Moore and W. B. Yeats now first printed with an Introductory Note by William Becker. (Reprinted from *The Dublin Magazine,* April/June 1951)   1951
Wade No. 211b   U of R
This is an offprint from *The Dublin Magazine.*

157 **The Collected Plays** of W. B. Yeats
Macmillan and Co, Ltd   1952
Wade No. 211d   R S
This contains the contents of the 1934 volume of Collected Plays, to which are added five other plays.

158 **W. B. Yeats and T. Sturge Moore:** Their correspondence, 1901–1937
Edited by Ursula Bridge
Routledge & Kegan Paul Ltd   1953
Wade No. 340   R S

159 **Some Letters from W. B. Yeats to John O'Leary and His Sister from Originals in the Berg Collection**
Edited by Allan Wade
The New York Public Library   1953
Wade No. 211f   U of R
300 copies were printed.

160 **W. B. Yeats Letters to Katherine Tynan**
Edited by Roger McHugh
Dublin, Clonmore and Reynolds Ltd
London, Burns Oates and Washbourne Ltd   1953
Wade No. 211h   U of R

161 **The Letters of W. B. Yeats**
Edited by Allan Wade
Rupert Hart-Davis   1954
Wade No. 211j   R S

162 **W. B. Yeats Autobiographies**
Macmillan and Co, Ltd   1955
Wade No. 211l   R S

163 **A Vision**
By W. B. Yeats
A re-issue with the author's final revisions.
The Macmillan Company, New York   1956
Wade No. 211m   R S

164 **The Variorum Edition** of the Poems of W. B. Yeats
Edited by Peter Allt, late of Trinity College, Dublin and Russell K. Alspach, United States Military Academy
The Macmillan Company, New York   1957
Wade No. 211n   R S

165 **Mythologies**
By W. B. Yeats   1959
Macmillan and Co, Ltd   R S

166 **Essays and Introductions**
By W. B. Yeats   1961
Macmillan and Co, Ltd   R S

LIST OF LENDERS TO BOOKS AND MANUSCRIPTS SECTION

Dublin, Trinity College Library: 4, 8, 13, 25, 27, 28, 30, 33, 36, 37, 38, 43, 46, 49, 58, 74, 75, 78, 80, 84, 86, 98, 103, 109, 111, 113, 115, 120, 125, 129, 131, 132, 134, 135, 137, 138, 139, 140, 142, 143, 145, 147, 150.

Leeds University, Brotherton Library: 50, 51, 81.

Reading University Library: 1, 2, 3, 5, 9, 11, 12, 14, 15, 17a, 19, 20, 22, 23, 24, 28, 34, 39, 41, 60, 61, 62, 67, 77, 79, 89, 90, 92, 93, 94, 96, 99, 102, 104, 105, 106, 110, 116, 117, 123, 127, 128, 133, 144, 149, 151, 154, 155, 156, 159, 160.

Robin Skelton, Esq: 6, 7, 10, 16, 17, 18, 21, 26, 29, 31, 32, 35, 40, 42, 44, 45, 47, 48, 52, 53, 54, 55, 56, 57, 58a, 59, 60, 63, 64, 65, 66, 68, 69, 70, 71, 72, 73, 76, 82, 83, 85, 87, 88, 91, 95, 97, 100, 101, 107, 108, 112, 114, 118, 119, 121, 122, 124, 126, 130, 136, 141, 146, 148, 152, 153, 157, 158, 161, 162, 163, 164, 165, 166.